EUROPE
IN A
SHRINKING WORLD

A TECHNOLOGICAL PERSPECTIVE

EUROPE
IN A
SHRINKING WORLD

A TECHNOLOGICAL PERSPECTIVE

Laurance Douglas Reed

OLDBOURNE · LONDON

OLDBOURNE BOOK CO LTD
2 PORTMAN STREET LONDON W. 1 .

© LAURANCE REED 1967

PRINTED IN GREAT BRITAIN BY
WILLMER BROTHERS LIMITED
BIRKENHEAD

PREFACE

This book had its origin in a debate in the Oxford Union in the autumn of 1962. In making preparations for a speech in favour of the political aims of the Common Market I came to appreciate the importance of the European movement as a new method of establishing international order. I determined that on going down from Oxford I would spend a year in the Community making my own assessment. I went to Brussels in October, 1963. While over there I became very interested in the technological perspective, a question which, at that time, had been neglected by students of European integration. Encouraged by friends, I started to write a book on the subject. A study of 12 months became a work of $3\frac{1}{2}$ years – much of it passed in the capitals of the Six, and other international centres in Europe.

Science and technology is the talking point in Europe, and a book on the subject seems very timely, especially now that Britain has decided to try to obtain entry to the Common Market again. Alarmed at the growing 'Technology Gap' between the two sides of the Atlantic, European leaders have new cause for speeding the economic and political unification of their countries. At the same time the case for British entry has been reinforced. Many ideas and plans are now in the air on ways and means of strengthening Europe technologically. Events are moving swiftly and new, more accurate information on the subject is being brought to light each month. In this book I have tried to marshall the facts and to advance the argument a little. But I have also attempted to place the movement to unite Europe in a wider perspective, and to consider it as a response to technological pressures. More specifically, it is a study of technology as an integrating force in international relations, and of the potentialities of the Community in giving effect to the dimensions modern technology requires. Quite the best work in unearthing information has been done by the

Scientific Directorate of OECD and I have relied heavily on their material.

During the course of this study I have interviewed a very large number of people who were kind enough to give me their time – scientists, engineers, industrialists, politicians, journalists, economists, professors, soldiers, diplomatists, lawyers, and *fonctionnaires* of every kind. It has been my general impression that the majority of scientists have little interest in, or idea of, the political and economic significance of their work, and equally that the majority of non-scientists have little idea of the problems and prospects of science – if they fully appreciated the value and importance of science in our society at all. The exceptions were almost always Frenchmen who, as a nation, it seems to me, have thought out the future more thoroughly than any other European country. As a sample of their thinking I recommend Louis Armand's remarkable book, *Plaidoyer pour L'Avenir* (Calmann-Levy, Paris 1961).

For encouraging, advising and assisting me in various ways I should like to thank, M. et Mme D. Braun, Professor Henri Brugmans, Mme E. Bubba, M. Antonio Ducci, Mr Thomas Fina, Mr and Mrs J. Harned, Mr and Mrs R. Harrison, Mr John Lambert, Mr Russell Lewis, M. Manfredo Macioti, Mr Richard Mayne, Mr and Mrs D. Mclaughlin, Mr and Mrs J. Moore, Mr Michael Palmer, Mr and Mrs M. Parker-Brady, Mr John Pinder, Mr and Mrs D. Reed, Professor I. Samkalden, Mr John Swift, M. Jacques Vandamme, the Director and staff of the European Communities Information Service in London, Austin Reed International Ltd, and my publishers.

London, June 1967   *L.D.R.*

CONTENTS

'. . . the question, whether large states or small states are best, is not one which can be answered or ought to be discussed absolutely. We often hear abstract panegyrics upon the happiness of small states. But observe that a small state among small states is one thing and a small state among large states quite another. Nothing is more delightful than to read of the bright days of Athens and Florence, but those bright days lasted only so long as the states with which Athens and Florence had to do were states on a similar scale of magnitude. Both states sank at once as soon as large country-states of consolidated strength grew up in their neighbourhood. The lustre of Athens grew pale as soon as Macedonia rose, and Charles v speedily brought to an end the great days of Florence. Now if it be true that a larger type of state than any hitherto known is springing up in the world, is this not a serious consideration for those states which rise only to the old level of magnitude?'

J. R. Seeley, 1885.

Chapter I

A Shrinking World

The growth of nations in size is an established trend in history. No consistent or unbroken sequence is traceable in this expansion, but a general tendency towards larger aggregates of power is quite evident. The movement is confirmed by the successive compounding of human associations into ever wider circles – the family to the clan, the clan to the tribe, the tribe to the nation, the nation to the state, the state to the regional grouping. Certainly, there are few countries now that are not amalgamations of smaller political units organized at some degree of intensity or other. Britain is a unitary state of four nations; America a federation of fifty states; Switzerland a confederation of twenty-two cantons; the Soviet Union has sixteen republics; West Germany eleven laender; and so on.

Most of these combinations were formed in the relatively recent past. Britain was united by the *Act of Union* which conjoined England and Scotland in 1707. Italy had her *Risorgimento* in the 1860's. The shape of the United States was settled in the same decade. The German Reich was proclaimed in 1871. Germany indeed, as recently as the *Treaty of Westphalia* (1648), consisted of no less than three hundred and fifty separate, self-assertive, sovereign bodies, and even the Germanic Confederation of 1815 had thirty-five autonomous states. The view that there is something fixed and settled about existing political arrangements is not supported by historical precedent.

In the olden days the foundations of political union were often laid in the nuptial beds of dynastic families. The marriage of Ferdinand and Isabella (1469) united the two realms of Castile and Aragon and paved the way for a hundred and fifty years of Spanish supremacy. At other times purchase has been important. America acquired Louisiana from the French (1803), and Alaska from the Russians (1867), adding more than a million and a half square miles to her territory for the trifling outlay of 35 million dollars – a tidy deal for an area fifteen times the size of Britain. On rare occasions, originating usually as a defensive league, mergers have even come about through the voluntary assent of several nations. But the chief instrument in enlarging the size of states has always been war. The world's empires were welded together in this way and so too were many modern states like Britain, Italy and Germany. Initially, each acquired unity as a result of a military victory by some part of what became a single nation. In Britain it was the work of the English; in Italy of the Piedmontese; and in Germany of the Prussians.

Military superiority, of course, was a decisive factor in expansion by war. A marked technological advantage increased a group's powers of conquest many fold. A few hundred *Conquistadors* with superior equipment conquered an empire. It took only six hundred against the Aztecs, and two hundred against the Incas. Apparently, the purchase of firearms from Dutch settlers brought a twenty-five-fold increase in the territory controlled by the Iroquois Indians. It is tempting, indeed, to try to establish a correlation between size and technical advance to show that the growth of political areas conforms to developments in weapons technology; but it is impossible to identify the contribution of individual innovations from technological progress in general. The most that can be said is that with technical improvements it has been possible for the dominant groups in history to govern, progressively, wider areas. One authority gives the following figures for the East: –

| 1900 BC | Hsia Dynasty | 52 000 sq. miles. |
| 1300 BC | Shang Dynasty | 307 000 sq. miles. |

500 BC	Chou Dynasty	608 000 sq. miles.
225 BC	Tsin Dynasty	1 021 000 sq. miles
100 AD	Han Dynasty	2 690 000 sq. miles.
668 AD	Tang Dynasty	4 750 000 sq. miles.
1290 AD	Genghis Khan	9 208 000 sq. miles.

In the West, the Roman Empire at its height embraced about two million square miles; the Spanish Empire held sway over five and a half million; and the British Empire over more than fourteen million.[1]

The unity of force, however, does not provide the basis for stable, enduring human associations. All these empires were unstable and transient. Racked by local insurrections from start to finish they eventually disintegrated through the rise to prominence and power of some individual province or other. Several empires indeed, like those of Attila and Alexander, rested solely on the personal prestige of a great warrior and broke up on their deaths.

A group of nations reduced to unity by force is only fused into a genuine, abiding community when the victor succeeds in generating in the vanquished a sense of loyalty which remains after the power or will to compel obedience has gone. Pure dominion is not enough. Laws are efficacious only when they are accepted implicitly; when the authority of the state is seen not primarily as the authority of law and force but as the authority of the community itself. In other words, a real society is founded on a sense of participation and consent rather than obedience and compliance. On a feeling of 'involvement'.

The fear of some common foe was one motive which often induced this sense of loyalty in larger groups. The Ancient Britons fiercely resisted the Roman invader, yet when in 442 AD, Rome came finally to withdraw her legions to face the threat of barbarian inroads nearer home, the Britons actually petitioned for the soldiers' return. But fear or hostility or opposition to some external menace is a negative motive, and one which ceases to be operative at the moment of victory. The cohesion it supplies is artificial, and as a basis for an abiding

association it is as unsound as compulsion. We have evidence
of this in modern times. India and Nigeria were once little more
than geographical expressions. They were brought to nation-
hood by foreign intervention, and their people found their identity as Indians and Nigerians through common resistance to
colonial occupation. Since the British withdrawal, however,
both countries have been hard put to it to prevent the national
fabric from falling apart in the face of more particularist interests and claims.

The instability of large states in the past was due largely to
technical causes. Communications are the groundwork of any
kind of solidarity or integration in a community organized on
a peaceful basis and the permanence of a nation is a function
of these cohesive ties. They are the tools for creating consensus,
fostering homogeneity and promoting a feeling of belonging
and involvement which dispose the members of a community
to cooperate and subordinate themselves to a single organization. But geographical barriers form an effective break to social
continuity, and in the past the shortcomings of communication
techniques in overcoming these dislocating factors set limits
to the size at which a community could be organized – a size
well below that attainable by force of arms. The technology
did not exist to consolidate the area of conquest into a permanent association.

TECHNOLOGICAL LIMITATIONS.

One serious defect in communications which restricted its
area of contact was the necessity of relying on *transportation*
(physical communications) to transfer and diffuse *information*
(intellectual communication). Messages had to be carried by
runners and riders so that the maximum speed of transmission
was equal to the top speed of transport. Probably the swiftest
information service was the homeing pigeon which Genghis
Khan employed to carry post from Europe to his Mogul capital
east of the Ural mountains.

To this rule of reliance there was the partial exception of
signalling by relay – a device used by many ancient communi-

ties with the aid of smoke, drums, reflectors and the like. The
Incas of Peru, the civilizations of the Indus Valley, the Chinese
and the Greeks all had quite elaborate systems. This method
of passing information has even been used to compete with
quite modern forms of transport. It is said, for instance, that it
was through the jungle telegraph that news of Queen Victoria's
death reached parts of Africa ahead of the ship bearing the
news.

During the Napoleonic wars, the French engineer, Claude
Chappe, set up a series of semaphore posts at ten mile intervals
between Paris and the frontier. Eventually, the network spread
over three thousand miles and through it news of events in
Munich could reach Paris on the same day. For military communication it was sufficiently impressive for the British and
Prussians to copy it. The Admiralty in London was linked to
the three southern naval bases, Chatham, Portsmouth and
Plymouth. A chain of eleven stations ran between Whitehall
and Portsmouth, passing through Semaphore Hill in Guildford,
messages were flashed seventy miles in seven minutes. The system was discontinued in 1847 when it was replaced by the
electric telegraph; although the use of semaphore in British
ships at sea only ended in 1966.

The utility of signalling for military intelligence cannot be
disputed, but its influence in promoting political cohesion was
negligible. It ran on a point-to-point basis through posts that had
to be within visual range or ear-shot. It was very vulnerable to
weather conditions, and though simple messages could be relayed at great speed by a pre-arranged code, complex information could not.

The cohesive strength of transportation itself was curtailed
by its dependence on two prime-movers: the animate energy
of man and beast and the inanimate energy of wind and water.
Wheeled vehicles were in use in Mesopotamia in the third
millenium BC, although the horse to drive them does not seem
to have been introduced much before 1600 BC. The horse then
remained the most efficient and rapid means of overland transport for 3 500 years thereafter. The sail was even older and

remained supreme at sea until the second half of the last century.

Both forms of energy had serious deficiencies for transport. From neither was it possible to obtain great speeds – essential in combatting the isolating influence of distance, and both were extremely irregular. Muscular energy, though reliable, is quickly exhausted – a horse ridden post-haste has to be changed every fifteen miles or so. On the other hand, wind power is inexhaustible but quite unreliable, and where certainty was essential, the sail had to be supplemented by the muscular energy of slaves – as in ships of war like the trireme.

The reliable range of transportation was greatly extended by technical improvements prior to the 19th century, and consequently there was a progressive increase in the size of area over which effective organization was possible. At sea there were exceptional exploits like the Phoenicians' circumnavigation of Africa and Leif Ericsson's passage to Vinland, but all regular traffic was confined to coasts, inland seas and river systems until a series of inventions at the beginning of the second millennium AD made deep-sea navigation practicable. The old two-oar lateral rudder was replaced by the fixed-stern rudder around the 12th century. With the old method it was impossible to steer really heavy ships and impossible to tack into the wind. The new method, together with the introduction of the jib, made it possible to take advantage of any wind. By the 16th century wind power was sufficiently mastered for auxiliary muscular energy to be discarded. The Battle of Lepanto (1571) was the last sea-fight in which there was a large-scale use of oars. The Spanish Armada, seventeen years later, had only four galleys out of one hundred and two vessels. Another important invention of the period was the mariners' compass. This lent some science to the art of navigation and opened the way to the great adventures of Diaz, Columbus, Vespucci, da Gama, the Cabots and Magellan, and led eventually to the expansion of Europe overseas.

On land the versatility of the horse was enhanced by breeding, the introduction of the iron horse-shoe and stirrups (10th century?) and, most notably, a new method of harness devised in Europe in the 12th century although known to the Chinese in 200 BC. The old method, by compressing the wind-pipe, reduced the traction of the horse to a third of its potential. Another important development in surface transport was the extension of combined wind-water-horse power, already exploited on river systems, by the building of canals. Bulk cargoes were always more easily handled on water. Adam Smith, the economist, noted that in his day one ship voyaging from Edinburgh to London could carry a load which overland would require fifty waggons pulled by four hundred horses. The Low Countries, taking advantage of their flat landscape, connected all their major cities by canals and by the 17th century had the most integrated transport system in the world. Canal construction on less even terrain had to await a general increase in engineering competence. In England work was pioneered by the Duke of Bridgewater and James Brindley in the middle of the 18th century. Four thousand miles of waterway liberated land-locked areas and revolutionized the conveyance of heavy commodities overland. It was an essential precondition for take-off towards industrialization.

These innovations accelerated the general circulation of men, their ideas and products and constantly enlarged the territorial scope of communications as a cohesive force. But not one of these developments harnessed a new source of power. They only gave more efficient control over existing prime-movers and consequently never wholly overcame the defects inherent in them. Each stage of transport development continued to set definite limits to size. Communications over any distance stayed infrequent, unreliable and insecure, and above all speeds remained low.

Probably the fastest speed ever attained on land before the Railway Age was the 50 mph of the 16th century Dutch ice-yachts. The fastest speed recorded for a runner over a hundred yard dash is 26.22 mph, and the greatest distance covered in an hour, $12\frac{1}{2}$ miles. Darius the Great of Persia had the finest system of runners of the ancient world. According to contemporary accounts, couriers relayed messages from Sardis on the Aegean, to his capital, Susa, at the top of the Persian Gulf, a distance of 1 700 miles, in eight days. Harold of England marched a whole army in five days from London to Stamford Bridge, Yorks. (200 miles) to surprise Harald Hardrada – it was considered one of the feats of the age. The fastest speed recorded for a horse is 43.26 mph over a quarter of a mile (according to the *Guinness Book of Records*). Beyond a mile it can do about 35 mph flat out although it certainly cannot keep that up for an hour. The Pony Express, operated by the Overland Mail Co. in 1860, ran from St Joseph, Missouri, to Sacramento, California. Riders rode night and day, seventy-five miles at a stretch and changed horses every fifteen to twenty. The schedule was eight days, and the fastest time seven days, seventeen hours.

Speeds at sea rarely exceeded 22 knots, and the longest day's run recorded under sail was 472 miles. During the California gold rush of 1851, the American clipper *Flying Cloud* set the record of eighty-nine days from New York to San Fransisco via Cape Horn. The coveted *Blue Riband* across the Atlantic was held by the *Sovereign of the Seas*, thirteen days, fourteen hours, and the winner of the Great Tea Race of 1866 did the 16 000 miles from Foochow to London in ninety-nine days.

These were occasional journeys of exceptional speeds, many of them done when these modes of transport were reaching the limits of their technical performance. The average rate of travel was far slower. In the 18th century a coach averaged 5 mph and a sailing ship 15 knots. On land thirty-five miles a day was considered good doing. It took longer to go from London to Bristol than it now takes to go by sea from Southampton to New York. The traveller from Sardis to Susa took not eight days but ninety. The eight day schedule of the Pony Express was exactly twenty-four days faster than Butterfield's overland stage. Emigrants to Australia took at least sixteen weeks and the waggon-trains rolling West across America, eight months.

Energy was the key to development. So long as the propagation of information was tied to transport, and transport depended on the horse and sail for its motive power, the size of communities was effectively restricted. Large political units were based, of necessity, on the idea of dominance which led only to a superficial, pseudo unity. No fundamental synthesis was ever reached. It is this technological factor which determined the partial, disparate, discontinuous character of civilization. Inland settlements were sporadic, land-locked, isolated and self-contained. Economic activity was fringed along natural highways provided by coasts and rivers. Interiors remained undeveloped.

*

The decade of the 1830's is crucial in the history of technology. It brought us steam, a new motive power which enabled transport to conquer its principal weakness – irregularity. It also brought us the electric telegraph, the first technique to release the 'conveyance of thought' from its dependence on transportation. If any period in history is to be taken as the divide between the ancient and modern it should be this. The contact techniques evolved then have totally transformed the scale of human economic and social operations, advancing them from a local to a global basis.

THE TRANSPORT REVOLUTION.

The railroad was several centuries older than the locomotive. It was first usefully employed in mines with trucks drawn by muscular energy. The steam engine itself was developed after many years of experiment culminating in the tests of James Watt at the close of the 18th century; but credit for the first steam locomotive belongs to Richard Trevithick who built an engine that averaged 9 mph in 1804. Like the railroad it first proved its value in the mines. Early public railways used horse traction and the first to use locomotives was the Stockton to Darlington, an experimental line whose chief engineer was George Stephenson. The Railway Age really began in 1830 with the inauguration of the thirty-five mile double track, Manchester-to-Liverpool Railway. Thereafter, the new system

B

spread very rapidly. In December of that year the South Carolina Railroad was operating in America. In 1835 the Brussels-Malines line in Belgium and the Nuremburg-Fürth in Germany. In 1838 the Vienna-Florisdorf in Austria and the St Petersburg-Tsarkoe Zelo in Russia. In 1839 the Amsterdam-Haarlem in Holland and the Naples-Portici in Italy. In Germany, where the railway played such an important part in consolidating the nation, the first inter-state line, the Magdeburg to Leipzig, was connected in 1840. By the middle of the century Britain had six and a half thousand miles of track and America eight and a half thousand. By the close of the century the two countries had twenty thousand, and one hundred and ninety thousand miles, respectively.

The advantage of the railway was that it combined speed with regularity of service; the two qualities in which the road and canal were inescapably defective. At the Rainhill Trials in 1829 Stephensons' *Rocket* reached 30 mph without a load; thus from the start the speed of the train was close to the top speed of the horse, but because steam provided a steady, sustainable source of energy its performance over any distance was superior. By 1849 trains between London and Bristol averaged 50 mph; ten times the pace of the stagecoach. In 1866 Estrade's Locomotive reached 74 mph and by 1869, when the Union Pacific met the Central Pacific at Promontory, north of the Great Salt Lake, to complete the first transcontinental railroad, a journey of four months on horseback was cut to four days. By 1900 trains were doing over 120 mph and on the Trans-Siberian Railway, begun in 1891 and completed in 1917, the Moscow-Vladivostok Express today accomplishes the 6 000 mile journey in eight days – a journey that once took over a year. In 1955 a French electric train set the present record of 205 mph. Of course, regular runs are much slower. The fastest is the Tokyo-Osaka Express which covers the 320 mile journey at 100 mph; three hours, ten minutes. It is intended to reduce this to two and a half hours by 1970, and extensive trials for 125 mph runs have been made in both France and Germany.

The steam engine was also used to power boats. Almost certainly the first application was in a boat built by Denis Papin in 1707. He took his family for an outing on the Fulda, but some local oarsmen, fearful for their livelihood, broke up both the inventor and his vessel – an early example of obstruction to technical progress from vested interest. Although several experiments were made after that by French and British engineers, it was the American, Robert Fulton, who was the first successful pioneer a hundred years later. Fulton demonstrated a steam-driven paddle boat on the Seine, but its significance was lost on Napoleon and he returned to the United States where he built the *Clermont* which plied the Hudson River between Albany and New York. In 1812 Henry Bell's *Comet* enjoyed some commercial success on the Clyde. After the *Comet* steam navigation entered a period of continual progress. In 1819 an American ship, the *Savannah*, made the Atlantic crossing and this is often claimed as the first passage under steam. It was not until 1833 that the Atlantic was entirely crossed under steam; the Canadian built *Royal William* in thirty-six days. Regular traffic was opened by the *Sirius* in 1838, followed in a matter of hours by the *Great Western* which had completed the trip in fifteen days at 8 knots.

Early steam-powered vessels were paddle-driven and paddles were too easily smashed in rough seas to be satisfactory. They were also sluggish and could still be beaten by sail in a fair wind. A radical improvement was the screw, devised by a Swedish inventor, and used by Brunel in his *Great Britain*. Around the 1840's the sailing lines on the Atlantic averaged twenty-two days on the eastward journey and thirty-four days against the more contrary winds of the westward journey. But steam/screw had reduced the eastward journey to fifteen days amd cut the westward journey in half; a difference of seven and seventeen days, and good enough for the British government to award the mail contract to a steam line.

The problem for steam at this stage was not that it was slow or unreliable but that on long runs it was uneconomic. Coal took up far too much stowage and reduced the space left for cargo. The position was eased somewhat by setting up coaling stations around the world, and gradually the economics were altered by engineering advances, like the compound expansion engine, which made more efficient use of steam and reduced the amount of fuel that had to be carried. By the 1860's steamers, besides being more punctual and reliable in their movements, could do four times the stint of sail in a year, and clippers were definitely in retreat. The most important break-through of all in engine efficiency was Charles Parson's turbine. In 1897 his *Turbinia* showed up uninvited at the Jubilee Naval Review and made the rest of the fleet look foolish by cavorting through the formations at $34\frac{1}{2}$ knots. This invention, incorporated in the ocean liner, brought the Blue Riband down to five days in 1910. By 1952 this was further reduced to three days, ten hours.

The railway remained the dominant means of overland transport until the First World War. Several attempts were made to employ steam engines in road vehicles but never successfully, and for a time both canal and road transportation were eclipsed. However, new prime-movers were eventually found for road transport as well. In the mid-1880's Daimler and Benz, simultaneously but independently, were working on the internal combustion engine using petrol, and in 1908 a German car traversed the United States from coast to coast. By 1914 Henry Ford's factories were producing a quarter of a million cars each year – almost equal the total number of cars Britain had on her roads at that stage. Today the world has some 160 million registered motor vehicles clocking up about 6 000 miles a year each. The road vehicle has the advantage over the train that it is more flexible and has now displaced rail for many types of conveyance. In particular, it has given unprecedented mobility to the individual – so much so indeed, that in the United States private cars now account for nine-tenths of all passenger movement.

But by far the most dramatic event in the transport revolution was the conquest of the third element. Air is a more universal medium than either land or sea, and aircraft ride freely, at great speed, over all geophysical hurdles. Air travel has done more than any other form of transportation to break up the isolating influence of distance and give human activity a global character and dimension.

A lot of experimentation – most of it disastrous, and some theory on aerodynamics was done in Europe in the last century, but the first powered, sustained, controlled flight by a heavier-than-air machine was achieved by the American Wright brothers in 1903 – a distance of 284 yards at an airspeed of 45 mph. Here again progress was exceedingly swift. By 1909 Bleriot had flown the Channel in 37 minutes. Ten years later Alcock and Brown flew the Atlantic non-stop, and in the same year (1919) the first international air service was opened between London and Paris. In 1920 London, Paris, Brussels and Amsterdam were linked together by a freight/passenger/mail service. In 1924 the first transcontinental airmail route was inaugurated between New York and San Francisco; a distance covered in 27 hours which compares with the semi-weekly 18-20 day mail service of sixty years before. In 1927 Lindberg flew non-stop from New York to Paris in $33\frac{1}{2}$ hours – reducing to hours what it had taken the sailing ships the same number of days. In 1934 Australia could be reached by air from England in 4 days – reducing to days what it had taken ships the same number of months. In 1949 an aircraft circumnavigated the globe in a mere 94 hours – a journey that had taken Magellan 3 years. Between 1924 and 1937 the time taken to traverse the breadth of the United States plummeted from 27 to $7\frac{1}{2}$ hours. In 1938 U.S. airlines carried nearly a million and a half passengers, by 1945 they were carrying thirteen million – a figure that was to be tripled again by 1955. A typical airliner before the war had a range of a thousand miles and carried twenty passengers at 180 mph; the typical airliner of the mid-1950's had a range of three thousand miles and carried eighty passengers at 350 mph; today scheduled jet transports cruising above 500 mph carry more than a hundred passengers across America in under six hours and across the Atlantic in under eight.

Thus in a short 150 years since steam first took over from the sail and the horse the pace of human travel has been accelerated one hundred-fold. The scale of movement these developments have facilitated is hard to grasp. Some idea can be gained from the volume of traffic handled each year by the world's scheduled airflights, and from the international tourist flow. In 1965, beside carrying 4 billion cargo ton-kilometres and 1 million mail ton-kilometres, 177 million passengers were flown a total 199 billion passenger-kilometres. About half this was borne on international routes – 4 million people flew the Atlantic and 18 million flew on intra-European routes. In 1965, it is estimated that there were 75 million international tourists; tourism is the largest single item in international trade (in value) – amounting to about 10 per cent of the aggregate.[2]

Yet this revolution in movement is by no means over. New transportation methods are being devised, more dexterous, carrying greater loads at higher speeds. One of the more novel possibilities is the carriage of solids in pipelines. Bulk fluids, oil, gas and water are piped huge distances already, but much research has been done in the past few years into the practical possibility of using pipeline transmission for other commodities by using capsules propelled in liquids, or by compressed air – a principle similar to that employed in departmental stores. In 1957 a pilot scheme, 108 miles in length, operated by the Consolidated Coal Company of Pittsburg, demonstrated the feasibility of transfering solids suspended in liquids, while in Battersea, London, the Morgan Crucible plant has been handling graphite in pipes by pneumatic pressure for several years.[3]

The helicopter, the amphibious craft, VTOL flight and the hovercraft, are all examples of the growing versatility of modern forms of travel. The Westland SR.N4 hovercraft – to be in service on the Channel in 1968, will carry 220 passengers at 69 knots in fair sea conditions and designers now envisage long-range hoverliners of up to 4 000 tons, with passenger-freight capacity of 1 600 tons, speeds up to 50 knots on sea routes of 2 000 nautical miles. The only physical boundary not yet mastered by man-made vehicles is the interface between air and water. In this case the Convair division of General Dynamics have conducted a feasibility study into the concept of the submersible plane and claim that it is not only practicable but well within the state of the art.

Only a few years ago Japanese experts were predicting that the maximum size of tankers in the future would not exceed 200 000 tons but the *Idemitsu Maru* of 209 000 tons is already at sea and a 276 000 tonner has been laid down in a Japanese shipyard. Even larger ones are now in prospect. Container ships are another development that are about to revolutionize North Atlantic trade. An Anglo-U.S. experiment in container shipment of cargoes from March to June 1966 cut the transit time between Illinois and Glasgow by nine days and reduced the time between Birmingham and Chicago from nineteen to fourteen days. It is expected that the new births will handle about ten times the annual quantity of freight of traditional ones. Certainly rigorous innovation will be necessary if shipping is to keep pace with the freight carrying potential of a new generation of aircraft. Present airliner loads do not exceed 180 passengers but the 'jumbo' jets now being ordered by airlines for the early 1970's, like the Boeing 747, will carry as many as 500 passengers. Russia is building a 720 passenger version of her AN 22 for non-stop airbus services across the breadth of the Soviet Union.

Yet still the greatest gains must be expected from the reduction in travel times. The Anglo-French *Concorde* supersonic jet airliner, to be in service in 1971, will carry 136 people at Mach 2.2 (Mach = 760.98 mph, the speed of sound at sea level) and bring New York within three and a half hours of London. Russia's TU 144 with a smaller load will go slightly faster, while America's supersonic transport (SST) will follow two to three years behind *Concorde*, but fly 400 mph faster. Dazzling though these technological achievements are they will soon be eclipsed by hypersonic flight on which the American and European aircraft industries have already put in a great deal of work. Ramjet engines have been developed to operate in the Mach 2–5 range and in California the Marquardt Corporation is working to perfect a scramjet to operate in the Mach 5–8 range (up to 5 300 mph). Beyond this, the Missile/Space Systems

Division of the Douglas Aircraft Co. have done a study on a re-usable one stage rocket ship capable of verticle take-off. It would coast out of the atmosphere in an arc, attaining a maximum height of 125 miles, and do the greater part of the trip above the atmosphere where there are no drag problems. *Pegasus*, as this project is called, would carry 260 passengers at 17 000 mph – seven times faster than projected SST's. A journey that would take present day jets 6.8 hours and SST's 2.2 hours would take *Pegasus* only 26 minutes and bring the very furthest point of the globe within 45 minutes.[4] The Douglas Company believes that it could be a reality of the 1980's.

However, there is one development which might upset this prediction – the no less spectacular progress in telecommunications which call into question the value of actual physical presence for many kinds of transaction where for the moment this is thought essential.

THE INFORMATION EXPLOSION.

When the golden spike was driven in at Promontory to connect the final link in America's transcontinental railroad, news of the event was flashed instantaneously to the east and west coasts by the electric telegraph. Ever since the 1750's schemes had been put forward for using electromagnetic phenomena for long distance communication. Alessandro Volta's electric battery, the first source of electricity which could produce a continuous flow of energy, brought the whole idea nearer practical realization and other ingredients were supplied by Oersted and Ampère. The commercial development of the telegraph in England was pioneered by Cooke and Wheatstone who entered into partnership in 1836, took out their first patent in 1837, and the next year persuaded the Great Western Railway to adopt their system. It was first tried out between Paddington and West Drayton and quickly showed its worth. Simultaneously, but independently, in America, Samuel Morse devised a cheaper, and technically superior system. After some resistance, Morse obtained the funds from Congress to establish an experimental line, Baltimore-Washington (forty miles), in 1844.

To begin with insulation problems caused constant breakdowns and early telegraph lines spent as much as half their time out of action. Eventually this fault was cured and the economics of the technique were improved when more convenient means of generating and recording signals increased the speed of transmission. Ways were also found of 'multiplexing' – sending more than one signal at once. Edison produced a quadruplex telegraph that sent two messages in each direction at the same time.

Once the utility of the telegraph had been demonstrated experimentally, the rate of installation of new line was very rapid indeed on both sides of the Atlantic. By 1848 Florida was the only state in America east of the Mississippi where the telegraph had not reached. In 1851 a cross-Channel cable linked London and Paris. In 1861 the Pony Express was put out of business by the first transcontinental line, and by then the world had 150 000 miles of telegraph in use, of which Europe had 95 000 and America 48 000.

Submarine cables of great length, like the 1 600 mile Atlantic cable, posed special physical and electrical difficulties. One snag was caused by capacitance, a tendency for the cable to dissipate the signal rather than passing it along. Messages were retarded, and the amount of information which could be transmitted in an hour so small that it threatened to make the whole venture uneconomic. This hitch was temporarily avoided by providing a more sensitive receiver – Thomson's galvanometer. After four abortive attempts the first permanently successful cable was established in 1866. Six years later a further four had been laid. In 1871 the Indo-European line was strung, and by 1872, only forty years since Morse had begun work, the Mayor of Adelaide exchanged messages with the Lord Mayor of London and the first set of world-wide links were complete.

The telegraph released communications from their reliance on transportation and brought some of the remotest parts of the world into immediate contact, but the necessity of coding the transmission prevented it from ever becoming a convenient means of communication between individuals. This was provided when the direct transmission of speech was achieved. The invention of the telephone, like so many inventions, drew heavily from the work of others. According to the British and American courts who were called upon to decide the issue in a series of patent cases, the first practical instrument was the work of Alexander Graham Bell and certainly it was he who first began to exploit the telephone commercially under a patent granted in 1876. In England it was described by *The Times* as the 'latest American humbug', a view that seems to have been shared by a majority of its readers. In 1884 Britain could boast only 11 000 phones as against 148 000 in America, and this gap has never been closed. Today Britain has some 11 million phones handling over 16 million conversations daily compared to America's 84 million taking 240 million conversations daily. The entire American network consists of 260 000 miles of route, containing 35 million miles of wire, fusing together 75 000 communities. It links its subscribers to 98 per cent of the world's 200 million odd telephones which are presently increasing at the rate of 12 million a year.

Before this sort of expansion was possible a number of technical problems associated with long distance telephony had to be solved. Due to the attenuating characteristics of conductors, speech when passing along a wire decreases in strength so that beyond a certain distance it becomes too weak to actuate a receiver. Capacitance is the most serious source of attentuation but whereas it delays the transmission of current in the telegraph only over very long lines, in telephony the problem is appreciable over much shorter distances. Two ways were devised for overcoming this obstacle. The first was to improve the transmission of the voice by loading the lines with inductance to compensate for the effect of capacitance. The other method was to use boosters or repeaters to amplify the current at intervals along the line – a development made possible by the three-element vacuum tube. By 1914 the useful range of the telephone had been extended to 2 000 miles and the next year San Francisco and New York were hooked up over a 3 400 mile line.

Besides increasing the range of the phone, new techniques enormously increased the carrying capacity. Carrier-systems were one way in which circuit capacity was multiplied. In this system voice wave frequencies are transposed to a higher frequency range for transmission over the line. By using different carrier frequency bands a number of conversations can be transmitted simultaneously over one transmission path. In other words, to cope with increased traffic an extra number of lanes is provided. Carrier-systems were first commercially employed in 1918 when five conversations could be had on a single pair of wires, but with modern methods as many as sixteen telephone circuits can be derived from a single open-wire pair. The system has been further expanded in coaxial cables which carry a much greater volume of traffic than ordinary wires because they can handle a wider band of frequencies. In fact coaxials have been developed to the point where one cable can carry 32 400 telephone circuits at a time.

Another way of increasing capacity is to pack more conversations into a single channel. In *Time Assignment Speech Interpolation* (TASI) transmission links are assigned to the speaker only when he is talking. By utilizing idle time in the unused direction, as well as pauses between words and even syllables, capacity has been almost doubled.

Pulse Code Modulation (PCM) is yet another way of increasing existing capacity. It was invented as early as 1938 but is only just being applied. In this case speech is not transmitted in a continuously varying wave form as in earlier multiplexing techniques but in the form of a series of digital pulses. Information is sampled at 8 000 times a second and converted into a code. The transmission path is allocated to each channel in turn on a time sharing basis. At the receiving end the channels are separated and decoded into the original speech. This method promises to enable conversations to be even more densely interleaved.[5]

The technical problem of designing reliable, long-age repeaters prevented a transatlantic telephone cable from being laid until 1956. Initially, TAT 1. as it was named, provided 36 two-way voice channels but later this was increased to 48 channels. Since 1956 some 70 000 miles of undersea cables have been laid throughout the world; a further five cables beneath the North Atlantic. The newest, TAT 4. in 1965, provides 128 voice-circuits and was the first to link the United States direct with continental Europe. It brings the total capacity on the Atlantic to 600 odd circuits (employing TASI) although it is estimated that 2 100 circuits will be required in the area by 1975.[6] However, the first transatlantic conversation was held as early as 1915, and a regular telephone service commenced in 1927 – not by cable transmission links but by radio.

Wireless is an unrivalled instrument for long distance communication because it disposes of the necessity for physical contact between sending and receiving units. The idea of propagating intelligence through space on electromagnetic waves was suggested by Clark Maxwell's theory that light and electrical waves are identical, the difference being only one of wave length. The notion had been fostered earlier by the experiments of Michael Faraday. The theory was proved by the German physicist, Hertz, in 1885, and Edouard Branly devised a workable apparatus which could detect Hertzian waves. Early in the 1890's several scientists succeeded in sending signals by 'wireless' in their laboratories, but it was the Italian engineer, Guglielmo Marconi, who put wireless on a practical basis. Ignored by the Italian government Marconi came to England to collaborate with the GPO. He was granted an English patent in 1896 and the same year successfully demonstrated transmission over more than a mile. In subsequent trials on Salisbury Plain wireless distance was boosted to four miles, eight miles and then ten miles. By 1898 the first wireless cable for cash had been sent, and in 1899 the Channel was bridged.

From the outset many scientists argued that radio waves could not be transmitted beyond the earth's curvature (about 30 miles) and that consequently the oceans could not be spanned. But in 1901 Marconi proved them wrong by passing signals between Poldhu, Cornwall, and St John's, Newfoundland. It is not known how they were propagated. Ground waves are diffracted over the earth's surface and thus can provide communication between points hidden from each other by the horizon if high power and tall antennae are used. Marconi sent his messages from a 200 ft high mast to receiving antennae suspended 400 ft from a kite. However, it may be that Marconi was using short waves unwittingly, because later it was found that global coverage could be achieved by bouncing signals off the ionosphere – an ionized layer of the outer atmosphere that acts as a reflector for short radio waves. During the early 1950's sun-spot activity seriously unsettled the ionosphere; telephone talk became so noisy and capricious that it led to a considerable falling-off in transatlantic telephone traffic. It was this which finally induced the American Telephone and Telegraph Co., the British GPO, and the Canadian Overseas Telecommunications Corpn., to combine their technical resources and lay TAT 1.

Radio was first used for shipboard telegraphy and was instrumental in saving many lives at sea. Speech transmission was made possible by the thermionic valve – the result of work by Edison, Fleming and De Forest. Broadcasting itself grew spontaneously from amateur use. Official experimental broadcasts were made in Europe and America in the first years of the 1920's, and the BBC was set up in 1926. That year the world had $6\frac{1}{2}$ million receivers; today it has over 500 million, or 150 for every thousand people.[7] More than sixty countries operate external services. The output of the first five, in order of magnitude, Russia, China, the Voice of America, West Germany, and the BBC, amounts to more than 4 700 programme hours a week. The overseas services of the BBC, put out in some forty languages, are longer than its domestic radio and television services added together.

Television makes use of the same medium as radio. It had its beginnings with the discovery (1873) that the element selenium could convert the energy of light into electrical energy so that theoretically it could be used to transmit pictures. The next stage was the development by Nipkow of a 'scanning disc' by which an object could be dissected part by part and converted into electrical signals by the selenium photo cell. Baird used this mechanical method of scanning to demonstrate practical TV at the Royal Institute in 1926. By 1929 it was sufficiently advanced for the BBC to agree to regular experimental transmissions from London, but although this method was developed to quite a high degree of sophistication it proved in the end to be a technical cul-de-sac.

The modern electronic system we know originates from the inventions of Zworykin and Farnsworth which were developed by the Radio Corporation of America. But the roots of the system can be traced back to the proposals of Rosing, a professor of St Petersburg Technological Institute, and Campbell-Swinton, an English scientist, to use cathode-ray tubes for the transmission and reception of images. Although the basic inventions were made in America, television was first used for general broadcasting in England in 1936 using a system based on Zworykin's ideas and developed by a brilliant team of technicians at Electrical and Musical Industries Ltd. In America regular broadcasting began in 1941 and after the war television went ahead very quickly; 10 thousand sets in 1946, 4 million in 1950, 50 million in 1960. Today the world has approximately 177 million receivers or 51 for every thousand people.[8]

Television signals ride on high-frequency radio waves and are useful only over line-of-sight distances. Unlike radio, television cannot travel past the horizon unaided; either intermediate stations are required to relay signals or a direct physical connection is necessary – a coaxial cable with repeaters at eight mile intervals to restore the signal energy. The United States established a continental network using a microwave relay system in 1951. One hundred stations at 25 mile intervals were needed to complete the coast-to-coast circuit. In 1952 Britain and France were hooked-up via the Eiffel Tower and later other West European countries were linked through a combined microwave-coaxial network – Eurovision. Intercontinental exchanges were another matter. The Atlantic cables were of limited capacity and TV could not squeeze itself through them (a TV channel requires roughly 1 000 times the frequency bandwidth of a telephone channel). Technical considerations looked like restricting the international use of this media to a regional level at the highest.

In fact it was not so. As early as 1945 an English electronics engineer, Arthur Clarke, had suggested that artificial earth satellites on high orbits could act as relay stations to carry TV to the entire earth.[9] High-powered rockets, part of the dividend from the American-Soviet space race, have made this concept a reality. *Telstar I* was built by Bell Telephone Laboratories and launched in July 1962. Circling in a low elliptical orbit it transmitted TV and telephone signals between the old and new worlds through ground stations at Andover, Maine, Goonhilly Downs, England and Pleumeur-Bodou, Brittany. In its first four months of operation *Telstar* put out forty-seven international programmes and could reach 200 million people.

Low orbit satellites, like *Telstar* and its successors *Relay I* and *II*, can be used only during the brief periods (about 15 minutes) when they are in line-of-sight of their ground stations. For continuous use a series of at least twelve satellites, spaced at even intervals, would be required so as to ensure that one would always be in position to relay signals. The Hughes Aircraft Co. of California had a better idea; one closer to Clarke's original concept. A satellite placed 22 300 miles above the earth takes 24 hours to complete its orbit. It travels at a speed which keeps it in step with the earth's rotation and therefore appears 'fixed' in the sky, neither rising nor setting, in permanent line-of-sight for a whole hemisphere. Hughes' *Early Bird*, the first 'synchronous' satellite for commercial use, went into orbit in April 1965; with 240 two-way voice channels it doubled the transatlantic circuit capacity overnight. All by itself it blanketed a third of the globe – three such satellites would give world-wide coverage. *Intelsat* (International Consortium for Satellite Telecommunication) plans to have a global system in orbit in

1968, each satellite with a capacity of 1 200 two-way voice channels or four TV channels.

Thus again in a short 150 years since the electric telegraph first enabled us to outreach the limitations of our sight and hearing it is possible for every nation to have instant contact with every inhabitable spot on earth. The speed, frequency, reach and fidelity of communications has been constantly expanded to the point where intellectual exchange has truly planetary dimensions. The diffusion of ideas and information these techniques have facilitated is incalculable. Over four million transatlantic telephone conversations are held each year. More than 28 countries now have over half a million phones. The Canadians talk more than any other nation with 635.6 telephone conversations per person each year.[10] *Early Bird* provided a 500 million audience for the World Cup Final 1966. Yet like the revolution in transport this explosive increase in information exchange is by no means over.

Relay satellites envisaged for the future will carry as many as 50 000 channels; fitted with more powerful transmitters they will be able to beam television direct to domestic sets without the aid of ground stations. But even with their great potential satellites are unlikely to supersede undersea cables and other earth bound techniques. There is little doubt that in the global network of the future communication satellites and undersea cables will be complementary. Only a few years ago 80 channels was considered large capacity for underwater cables. Today 360 circuits is the accepted norm and a 480 circuit cable has just been laid beneath the North Sea. The American Bell research laboratories have completed trials on a prototype 720 circuit cable and one British development aims at 1 280 channels. Commonwealth cable links stretch across the Atlantic from Scotland to Newfoundland (CANTAT), then across Canada by microwave beam to Vancouver, and thence by submarine cable to Auckland and Sydney routed through Hawaii and Fiji (COMPAC) with a branch off to Hong Kong and Singapore (SEACOM). The South African government now plan to complete the missing link in this world chain by throwing a cable round Africa from Madras to Lisbon.

Until recently it was thought that repeater techniques would limit the bandwidths of a single coaxial tube to 2 700 telephone channels, but transistorized repeaters have increased their potential to 10 000 channels, permitting a 20 pair coaxial cable to carry as many as 200 000 telephone conversations simultaneously. At present a typical microwave carrier can bear 1 800 conversations or one TV programme, but research into hollow wave-guide conductors for transmission lines promise extremely wide bands of frequencies. It is calculated that a single circular wave-guide 2 inches in diameter, and employing multiplex techniques, could carry about 100 000 telephone circuits.[11] Guided propagation has the added advantage over free propagation that it avoids spectrum congestion. The same frequency can be used over and over again without causing interference in other systems.

This enhanced capacity is needed to cope with the upsurge in demand for telecommunication facilities created by new services; video-phones, colour TV, educational TV, closed circuit TV and so forth. The immediate call is for additional data transmission links. Data has already been exchanged between continents via satellite and the Bell Company of America believes that within 15 years data transmission over all communication channels will equal that of speech. Eventually, information of all sorts stored in giant computers will be made available to the ordinary subscriber, diffused through a national grid and linked to an international information system.[12]

Facsimile transmission has been used for years to obtain instant photographs of distant events. More recently it has been used to achieve almost simultaneous printing of identical editions of newspapers thousands of miles apart; revolutionizing distribution. Japan's *Asahi Shimbun* was the first to employ this technique in 1959. At one time this paper used to reach Sapporo, North Island, two days after publication 500 miles away in Tokyo. Today it is on the streets of Sapporo one and a half hours after the Tokyo edition. The system is now in use in

c

eight different countries and ultimately this technique may be used to print newspapers directly in the home.

But by far the most stunning prospect, on which scientists are now working, is the possibility that the light end of the electro-magnetic spectrum can be added to the usable channels of com-munication. For 70 years scientists have been working their way up the radio part of the spectrum. Progress has yielded ever wider bandwidths and therefore, because the rate at which information can be transmitted is proportional to the width of the frequency, ever increasing capacity. Between the micro-wave part of the spectrum and the visible part there is a factor of ten thousand times. Optical wavelengths therefore offer enormous signalling capacity. Unfortunately, it is impossible to use optical frequencies for communications except by varying the amplitude of a light beam; as for instance when flashing a lamp. This is because light sources produce incoherent radia-tions which cannot be modulated so as to carry the imprint of messages. But with the Laser (*L*ight *A*mplification by *S*timu-lated *E*mission of *R*adiation) this can be done. It does produce a regular, coherent train of light waves. The system has already been tried out in space, but because of the inability of the Laser to penetrate fog, a practical system of Laser communications on earth would have to be beamed through a protected path analagous to a wave-guide pipe.[13] There are some daunting technical problems still to be solved but the *theoretical* ability of the Laser opens the prospect that a 1 000 million simultaneous telephone conversations could be carried on a single beam about the size of a candle's wick. Rather aptly it has been described as a 'solution looking for a problem'.[14]

But there remains one problem still searching for a solution. Despite these fabulous advances, languages remain a formid-able barrier to human communication. Switzerland is proof that this is not an insuperable obstacle to association at the political level but the linguistic factor is at the root of break-away movements in places like Canada with her French third, Belgium with her Flemish half, and India with her fifty languages. Communications have to accommodate themselves to the plurality of tongues, although they do help to reduce diversity by spreading the knowledge of languages more widely, and there are many instances where the language of the media have become the second language of the receiver. To some extent too, the visual propagation of ideas circumvents the problem, but no technique up to now has ever really satisfactorily overcome this obstruction to wider human solidarity. Yet here also, according to Sir Leon Bagrit., a solution is in sight. He predicts that personal miniaturized translating machines, pocket-size, will soon be available for face to face encounters or for incorporation in communication networks.[15]

*

In a burst of progress, compressed into a century and a half, man has evolved the technical means of global communication, destroying barriers and shrinking distances, knitting together the whole traversable surface of the planet. Our physical mobility has been extended by mechanical transport of great speed and suppleness, and our intellectual mobility enhanced by the immediacy and range of new contact techniques. Our activities, freed from their traditional bondage to nature, have been multiplied. From a world held *incommunicado* by feeble communications and organized, perforce, in small, disconnected little communities, we have moved into a world more highly integrated and interdependent. A world where, under the tightening embrace of technical bonds, nations have been brought into close physical contact and are being forged into larger intellectual and economic groupings. With the proliferation of techniques civilization has become more diffused and generalized, and the pattern of its development reversed; from the static to the dynamic, from the unintegrated to the integrated, from divergence to convergence, from the partial to the complete – a shrinking world in which the technological factor limiting the size of nations has been virtually eliminated. *Virtually*, because although the techniques are available, they are not yet adequately exploited.

Large tracks of the globe still remain untouched by these innovations and dependent on early prime-movers for their motive power. Nevertheless, the know-how does exist and there is no longer any *technological* obstruction limiting size, or indeed, preventing all the world from being welded into one peaceful unit. The parameters now are not technical but human. And that is a new fact in the world and one the political consequences of which our leaders have scarcely recognized.

Chapter II

The Dimensions of Technology

New technology has made large-scale human activity possible; but there is more to it than that. Contact techniques, by reason of their operational characteristics, are *inherently expansive*. It is not simply that they have facilitated the performance of large-scale economic, political, and military activities – they spontaneously enlarge the scope of human action by setting up their own level of operations; a level imposed by their functional rules and requirements.

Air transport is a graphic example. In this case the advantage of speed is reinforced by freedom from geographical hurdles which impede surface transports and force them to take circuitous routes (on average air distance in Europe is 30 per cent less than rail distance). Yet in spite of this superiority aircraft have done little to strengthen the internal cohesion of small states, whereas they have played a vital role in unifying continent-wide states like Russia. There are several reasons for this. On short stage distances an increase in speed does not result in any proportional decrease in flying times since a large part of the time is taken up with take-off and landing procedures, and the maximum cruising speed is reached for only a very short period. Account must also be taken of embarkation procedures and the journey time from city to airport at both ends: in air travel something like 60 per cent of total journey time, from city-centre to city-centre, is ground time. Consequently, below two hundred miles surface transport has the advantage, and from two hundred to four hundred miles the journey time differential is low enough to present air and rail travel as fairly close substitutes – all things being equal. Only above four hundred miles, and more positively above six hundred, is decreasing flying time of real significance. With supersonic transports the position is even clearer since economy in use depends on utilizing the SST's ability to fly long distances at great speeds. Furthermore, the time taken for these planes to climb to, and descend from, the height at which they fly, and to accelerate and decelerate at the speed at which they go (30 miles a minute), must be measured in literally hundreds of miles. Against small political scales, like those found in Europe, air transport is therefore, *by its very nature*, international in scope. And thus one result of increasing the speed of transport during the past 150 years has been not so much to shorten the time requirements of processes as to extend the area of the globe affected by them.

This dimensional aspect of technology is most pronounced in communication techniques; but it is not peculiar to them. It is common, to a greater or lesser extent, to all technologies. Each imposes its own geographical rules and modalities and the operational needs of an increasing number require a territorial expanse or *lebensraum* that is not paralleled within existing political contours as they are drawn in various areas of the world.

But this interplay between geography and technology, coupled with the general evolution of states in size, convinces many people that there is something inevitable in international adjustment to technological advance. According to this determinist school we are all bound to be organized into bigger and bigger blocks, and in the end, by the 'hidden hand' of technology itself, the world will be riveted into one harmonious and happy unit. Now this is nonsense. There is nothing *inevitable* about it. Technology may be spontaneous but political organization is not. Man-made boundaries do not automatically shift to suit the idiosyncracies of techniques. Technology may change the value of boundaries for the bounded area. It may diminish their relevance, alter their function, or even waterdown their divisive strength, and in this fashion technology may exert powerful pressures for the revision of political frontiers – but that is all. Modern techniques make large-scale political organizations possible; not certain.

To begin with the territorial demands of technology can be satisfied through simple collaboration between states – without the necessity of creating a new political entity at all. At the world level several specialized agencies of the United Nations exist to do just this. In the communications field, for instance, the *United Nations Educational, Scientific, Cultural Organization* (UNESCO) has some general responsibilities to promote the free flow of information, increase its circulation and supply, and help develop communication media and techniques. The *International Maritime Consultative Organization* (IMCO) advises on ways of cooperating in government regulations and practices relating to technical matters affecting the international shipping trade. The *Central Office for International Transport by Rail* has similar objectives in freight movement and passenger traffic by rail transport. The *International Civil Aviation Organization* (ICAO) develops the principles and techniques of international air navigation, fosters the planning of international air transport, ensures the orderly growth of international civil aviation and air navigation facilities, and standardizes practices dealing with communications systems, ground markings and airport rules of air traffic. ICAO recognizes that every state has complete and exclusive sovereignty over the airspace above its territory. The *Universal Postal Union*, on the other hand, goes so far as to state in its opening article that 'The countries between which the present Convention is concluded, form, under the title of *Universal Postal Union*, a *single postal territory* for the reciprocal exchange of correspondence'.

Perhaps the most important organization in international communications is the *International Telecommunications Union* (ITU) which maintains and extends cooperation in the improvement and rational use of telecommunications, and promotes the development of technical facilities and their efficient operation. The Union has a long history. The earliest case of international collaboration in this field is a bilateral agreement between Prussia and Austria in 1849. Similar agreements were concluded between Prussia and Saxony, and Austria and Bavaria, and in 1850 they were all merged to form the Austro-German Telegraph Union to which other German states and the Netherlands later adhered. At about the same time France made separate agreements with Belgium, Switzerland and Spain, and in 1855 these became the West European Telegraph Union. In 1852 three members of the group – Belgium, France and Prussia, signed a convention which in 1865 became the International Telegraph Union with eleven other nations adhering. Regulations on telephony were annexed to the convention twenty years later. Radio set up its own organization in 1906 and the two unions existed side by side until they agreed to amalgamate to form the International Telecommunications Union in 1932.

The ITU has been primarily concerned with the allocation of the radio frequency spectrum so as to avoid harmful interference between stations of different countries. Radio waves do not respect national frontiers. They have different propagation characteristics and different frequencies have different ranges. A high frequency station on one side of the world may cause serious disturbance to a station using the same frequencies on the other side. The proper use of the spectrum is, therefore, an international problem and integrated planning at a global level essential to obviate chaos on the ether. The Union, besides working to prevent interference, has also tried to allocate frequencies to different services – TV., radio, radio telegraphy and telephony, aeronautical and maritime radio, in such a way as to ensure that the frequencies employed are those with characteristics most suited to their functions. They have also tried to see that on the spectrum, an increasingly scarce commodity in the face of mounting international demand, no frequency stands idle at any time.

Technical disciplines require integration over wider and wider areas and in the communications field, at least, mutual accommodation has invariably been accorded. At a universal level, and especially at a regional level, we have an increasingly united and interdependent world. But if this is true in a purely technical sense it is patently untrue politically. For all these technical interconnections the world remains fragmented into hundreds of political units of unequal size and importance, each aiming at independence and each zealous of its sovereignty. Natural barriers have been erased but man-made, artificial ones have not.

TECHNICAL OPERATIONS.

Within the politically congested European area technical integration has already been carried a long way through inter-state arrangements. The earliest efforts at integrated planning were made on the international rivers, once the principal arteries of commerce. The *Central Commission for the Navigation of the Rhine* was created by the *Treaty of Vienna* (1815) and is by far and away the oldest international organization still in existence. The Commission is charged to ensure the observation of the principles of freedom of navigation in all technical as well as fiscal, customs, regulatory and judicial domains, on the 1 400 km from Basel to the open sea. A similar commission, set up by the *Congress of Paris* (1856), regulates the Danube as an international waterway between Ulm and the Black Sea.

Almost every economic organization there has ever been has had some responsibility for transport but some organizations have been more specifically technical. The *International Conference for Promoting Technical Uniformity in Railways,* for instance, was created in 1886 to investigate, from a technical point of view, how and under what conditions the conveyance of rolling stock from the rails of one state to another could be effected and facilitated. The most effective international body in the transport sector in recent years has been the *European Conference of Ministers of Transport* (ECMT), established in 1953. Its general purpose is to take measures necessary to achieve, at a general and regional level, the maximum use and most rational development of European inland transport of international importance. By an agreement concluded between ten national railway systems, known as *Europ Pool*, rail movements were facilitated by providing for the joint use of equipment throughout the continental area and the Ministers of Transport decided to extend this method of cooperation so as to cover the joint financing of the construction of railway waggons and the standardization of types. A special joint-stock company, known as *Eurofima*, was set up for the job and loans the stock to national railways as required. Another important initiative in easing international movement by rail was the *Trans-Europ Express* (TEE) agreement made in 1957. Under this agreement the necessity of changing locomotives at national boundaries was done away with, and a rapid continental service provided between 70 major cities, linked through 8 000 miles of track. The speed of travel was increased not so much by the trains going faster as by technical and operational improvements. In some cases journey times were reduced by as much as 40 per cent. The journey from Paris to Geneva, for instance, was cut from nine to six hours.

The *European Civil Aviation Conference* (ECAC) is the Ministers of Transport's counterpart in the aviation field. It exists to review the development of intra-European air transport with the object of promoting the coordination, the better utilization and the orderly development of such transport. *Air Union* is a more ambitious proposal, with aims similar to those of *Europ Pool*. It covers the pooling of operations, the joint use of maintenance facilities and the joint procurement of equipment between six national airlines. However, the idea has been at the talking stage ever since 1959. A strong bid was made in 1964 to get the project off the ground and bring it within the framework of the *European Economic Community* (EEC), but no agreement could be reached over the quotas for the various airlines, or over procurement procedures and policy, and the project lapsed. *Eurocontrol*, on the other hand, is in full swing. It provides for the most efficient use of international airspace. The organization has legal responsibility for the con-

trol of all general air traffic flying in the upper airspace over
Belgium, Holland, Luxembourg, West Germany, France and
the British Isles, where the density of movement is expected to
double by 1970. Supersonic flights will add an extra dimension
to air traffic control problems. Going from north to south a
supersonic transport (SST) will cross from one end of Belgium
to the other in only four minutes. Eurocontrol has built its own
experimental centre at Brétigny, near Paris, to simulate the
problems, and the experience gained will be embodied in an
upper airspace control centre to be built in Holland.

The entire infrastructure of physical communications in
Western Europe comprises some 2 million km of surfaced roads
of which 8 000 km are motorways, 225 000 km of railroad,
264 000 km of air route, and 36 000 km of waterway of which
15 000 km are canals. Increasingly, the technical operation of
them all is planned on a supra-national basis. Several projects,
recently completed, have considerably improved frontier interconnections. One of these was the canalization of the Moselle
with the Rhine between Coblenz and Thionville – a joint project of France, Germany and Luxembourg finished in 1964.
Two other projects pierce the Alps – Europe's most formidable
natural barrier. The Grand St Bernard Tunnel, linking Switzerland and Italy, was opened to all-the-year-round traffic in 1964,
and France and Italy were linked through the 11 kilometres
Mont Blanc Tunnel in 1965. There are several other ambitious
schemes designed to erase natural barriers to free movement.
There is a project to link Scandinavia with Denmark, and another to join Sicily to the boot of Italy across the Straits of
Messina. The Channel Tunnel, first conceived in 1802, has at
last moved beyond the conceptual stage. In 1964 something
like 27 million foreign cars entered Germany whereas a mere
91 thousand entered Britain; which shows what a considerable
obstacle to movement the Channel is.

There are two main bodies dealing with intellectual communications in Europe – the *European Conference of Posts
and Telecommunications*, and the *European Broadcasting
Union* (EBU). The former has essentially practical aims – the

harmonization and improvement of the administrative and technical services of its members. The EBU is not a governmental body but a professional association grouping Western Europe's radio and TV organizations. It does similar work to the ITU in planning the use of frequencies to avoid mutual interference – a particularly difficult problem in such a politically concentrated area. The Union's most spectacular achievement is *Eurovision*. It was in 1950 that the first important international TV relay took place between the BBC in London and *Radio-Diffusion Télévision Française* (RTF) in Calais. Paris and London were linked via the Eiffel Tower in 1952, and the next year France, the Netherlands and Germany were able to see the Coronation live from Westminster. Eurovision was then formed to cope with the technical planning of future relays, and put out its first programme, the World Cup Final, in 1954. The organization does not have its own network although this has been proposed. At the moment national networks are organized into an international network as required and planning for these exchanges is done through Eurovision's technical centre in Brussels. At the beginning of 1966 the organization grouped 18 countries with 2 823 broadcasting stations and 51 million sets between them, through 43 430 km of microwave and coaxial cable links. Eastern Europe has its own TV exchange body – *Intervision*, and programme exchanges between East and West are multiplying.

The most likely area of expansion in the future is the international interchange of information and data arising from the demand created by the internationalization of activities in medicine, banking, administration, travel, power production, retailing, education and business generally. A European Computer Grid is a distinct possibility for the 1970's.

ENERGY EXCHANGE.

Apart from this massive, articulated network of communications, there are several other important areas where Europe is already 'fused' in a purely technical way. Energy production is one of these. In the first stage of the industrial revolution the supply of energy was a major factor determining the location of industry. Coal is a solid, clumsy and cumbersome, and very costly to transport, and in the last century when coal was the primary source of energy industries grew up concentrated around the major deposits – the Midlands in England, the Ruhr in Germany. But today geographical factors have lost much of their importance. Primary energy in liquid or gaseous form, and secondary energy in electrical form, is light, flexible, easily transportable, and large blocks of energy are now transferred over extra long distances. An increasing proportion of these transfers find their way across national frontiers, without mobile carriage units as intermediaries, through power cables and trunk pipelines.

Since the war, the promotion of transfers of electric power across European frontiers has been the task of the Committee on Electric Power of the *United Nations Economic Commission for Europe* (ECE). In several cases at the start adjacent zones on each side of a frontier were linked by low-voltage lines before being connected to their own national networks. In recent years the process of interchange has been facilitated by technical advances in the use of higher voltages and the perfection of submarine direct current (dc) cables. Exchanges have reached a considerable pitch. There are at least 80 major transnational interconnections in Europe, which includes one across the Channel (Lydd-Echinghen) and several which pierce the Iron Curtain. Yugoslavia, for instance, has 110-kilovolt lines connecting with Austria and Italy in the west, and with Bulgaria, Hungary and Rumania in the east, and another 150-kilovolt line with Greece. Austria and Czechoslovakia have a 220-kilovolt line between them, and a similar line between Austria and Hungary is nearing completion. However, although these examples show that there is no exact demarcation, the general pattern has been for two large groups of grids to be built up corresponding to the East-West political division. In Eastern Europe there is an extensive future programme of interconnections which provides for large scale bulk transfers of power from Russia – independent of short-term operational needs. In

Western Europe, the *Union pour la Coordination de la Production et du Transport de l'Électricité* (UCPTE) provides an interconnected grid which acts as a single unit for operation. It covers an area from Jutland to Sicily, and from the Atlantic to the Yugoslav border. UCPTE has eight members, Belgium, France, Germany, Italy, Holland, Luxembourg, Austria and Switzerland, and has a transmission capacity of about 8 000 MW with a further capacity of about 1 500 MW with neighbours of the group. The total energy exchange between members runs at around 17 000 million kWh per year, or 3 per cent of production.

Many factors lead to these exchanges. First, and obviously, is the unevenness of natural resources against the unequal distribution of requirements. Europe's main hydro-power reserves are in the mountains of Scandinavia to the north, and the Pyrenees and Alps to the south. Between these two 'water' zones there is a middle region with few hydro-power reserves where electricity is generated by coal-fired or oil-fired (thermal) power stations. Transfers of power resulting from the uneven distribution of natural resources really amount to straightforward exports of power, but owing to power loss over extra long distance transmission bulk transfers of this kind do not yet amount to a very substantial proportion of total exchanges.

The basic reason encouraging exchanges is that it is operationally advantageous to do so. First, to meet contingencies – with transfers between countries it is easier to maintain the rhythm of supply when breakdowns occur or when repairs and overhauls become necessary. Second, to absorb 'overflows'. An 'overflow' is when excess rainfall produces a waterflow that can generate more electricity than a country or region can economically handle. Instead of allowing it to run to waste it is more profitable to convert it into electrical energy and transfer the surplus to a water deficit country. Here, it can either be fed direct into the grid, or, alternatively, it can be used for pumped storage schemes. The third operational advantage of international exchange arises from the daily and seasonal load diversity between one country and another. Electrical energy is shifted from areas with excess generating capacity to those facing a heavy drain. Daily and seasonal load diversity are both functions of geography. In the case of seasonal diversity the position is self-evident; in the case of daily diversity the position arises from the fact that peak loads tend to occur during the statutory period of twilight – the time between the setting of the sun and the time when the first stars begin to appear. Naurally, since each country has a different geographical situation, they have different twilight periods, and consequently there is a displacement between peak hours. In so far as the maximum simultaneous demand of a group of countries is therefore likely to be less than the sum of individual peak loads, it is possible for one country to compensate another during these hours. UCPTE uses a computer to ensure the rapid exchange of information on availability and need, and a good deal of forward planning is done.

The major blackout which knocked out electric power over an 80 000 square mile area of the north-east United States and Canada in November 1965 caused some misgivings about super grid systems. There have been several calls for a return to more localized production and consumption. However, the great leaps forward made recently in high-voltage direct current (hvdc) power transmissions seem certain to mean an expansion in really large-scale transfers over long distances in the future. Anyway, all existing hvdc projects are going ahead undaunted. Russia, which already has some 8 000 km of 500-kilovolt line, has been working on a 295 mile 800-kilovolt dc line between Volgagrad and Donbass. This is reported to be functioning well and the experience has given Russian engineers sufficient confidence to propose an all-Union power grid of up to 2 500-kilovolts, linking White Russia with Central Siberia and North Kazakhstan. In 1965 New Zealand went ahead with a scheme to join North and South Island with a 385 mile, 500-volt dc tie, and in the same year in Europe, Swedish electricity was connected to the continental power networks by a 250-kilovolt dc line that passed over the Island of Laeso to Denmark, and for the first time brought Scandinavia's considerable hydro-power reserves within reach of European industry. In 1966 Sardinia and Italy were joined via the French island of Corsica and plans are afoot for improving east-west European exchanges. In America a major 875 mile Pacific-Coast Intertie of 800-kilovolts will bring British Columbia's power to California in 1968. The Federal Power Commission has suggested that by 1980 the United States will need at least four east-west interties, each 2 000 odd miles in length and up to 1 500-kilovolts dc. In Europe again there is even a project to convert Iceland's water and geothermal resources into electrical energy and transmit it 500 miles by undersea dc cable to Scotland. For the more distant future it is just possible that power cables can be done away with altogether – large blocks of energy being transmitted instead by micro-wave beams.[1] Some comfort for the pylon haters.

The international construction of pipelines in Europe is a far more recent development than electricity exchange. Europe has about 30 000 miles of trunk pipeline as against well over a million miles in the United States where as much as 40 per cent of all energy used is transmitted by pipe. There, in the majority of cases, lines are used for gas, oil and oil products, although cane sugar and iron ore have been carried, and there are experiments in hand for wheat, wood pulp, sand and gravel. In Canada, Shell Canada Ltd. recently announced the world's first major solids pipeline to run from Alberta to the west coast. Russia is completing a 4 200 km 'Friendship Pipeline' to link her with East Germany, Poland, Czechoslovakia and Hungary. It originates on the river Volga, and crosses the Don, the Desna and Dnieper in Russia, the Bug, Narew, Vistula, Warta and Oder in Poland. The southern branch of this line parts at Mozyr, east of the Dnieper, and crosses the Carpathian Mountains into Czechoslovakia. Russia is now anxious to extend the system into Austria and Italy, and possibly even France.

Early natural gas finds in Europe, like those in northern Italy in 1926, and in southern France in 1939, were only distributed nationally. But not so the huge fields discovered in Holland and the North Sea. These are producing a dense tangle of pipelines interlacing Holland, Belgium, Germany and northern France – the 'cockpit' of Europe. There are also proposals for bringing Sahara natural gas by pipeline under the Mediterranean, up through Spain and Italy into the heart of the continent.

The first transnational oil pipeline to be completed was the Rotterdam to Cologne (RRP) of 180 miles, started in 1952, and later extended to Frankfurt. In 1960 came the 34 inch diameter South Europe Pipeline (SEPL), 485 miles in length, commencing from Lavera, near Marseilles, passing up to Strasbourg and then across the frontier into Karlsruhe, Germany, whence the 190 mile Rhine-Danube Pipeline (RDP 1963) links it with Inglostadt. In 1965 a pipeline from Genoa was finished to carry oil across Switzerland to Ulm, Germany, and thence to Ingolstadt. Yet another line to Ingolstadt is the new Transalpine pipe, 280 miles in length, being bored through the Alps from Trieste on the Adriatic. In 1966 the estimated tonnage passing through these routes was 70 million tons and by 1980 the total carrying capacity of an extended network is expected to exceed 150 million tons. Apart from new natural gas, oil and oil products pipelines, the installation of solids pipelines seems certain in the future. At the rate at which Europe is consuming and polluting her fresh water resources it also seems likely that pipelines will be built to transfer large volumes of water from water surplus to water deficit areas – a situation already obtaining in America.

An interesting example of transfrontier interconnection is to be found at the coal-chemical complext at Carling, Lorraine. Here, a network is being constructed which will permit German and French chemical works to exchange products by way of pipelines, the products crossing the frontier in both directions at the required stages of processing. Crude oil will be tapped from the SEPL near Strasbourg and carried by branch line to a refinery at Furstenhausen on the German side of the border. This refinery will produce naptha, and some 400 000 tons of this will be piped back to Carling each year where a plant will extract hydrogen and turn out 1 000 tons of ammonia a day.

D

Part of this output will be sent back along 47 kilometres of pipeline into Germany to a plant at Perl, and here the ammonia will be combined with carbon dioxide to produce urea. Forty per cent of this will find its way back again to Carling in solid form to be made into fertilizer.

SPATIAL PLANNING

Throughout Western Europe similar cases can be found where national frontiers are breached by technological operations. Another and particularly interesting example is at Meyrin, Geneva. Here, the *European Organization for Nuclear Research* (CERN) has erected a 28GeV (billion electron volts) proton synchrotron to do research on high energy particles. The machine is 200 metres in diameter and occupies 100 acres of Swiss soil bang on the French border. The Amaldi Working Party (1963), set up to advise on future European research in this field, proposed that the existing machine should be boosted to 56GeV equivalent by the addition of a pair of intersecting storage rings (ISR), 300 metres in diameter. The only space available for this is a 98 acre site contiguous to the present one, in French property on the other side of the frontier. The site has been acquired and when the appendage is functioning the machine will operate directly in two sovereign territories at once.

The example illustrates the necessity of international planning in the field of technological operations which require rather special topographical conditions. Among other suggestions of the Amaldi Working Party was a proposal that European countries should build a very large 300GeV proton smasher on a completely new site. The mean diameter of the main ring of this machine would be 2 400 metres ($1\frac{1}{2}$ miles) with a circumference of 7 500 metres (nearly $4\frac{3}{4}$ miles). To cope with other supporting buildings the whole site would have to afford 20 km² (roughly $7\frac{3}{4}$ sq. miles) and not be less than 4 km ($2\frac{1}{2}$ miles) in width. But apart from the sheer size of the area required, the locational and topographical conditions are rather exacting. The land would have to be uninhabited, give access to heavy loads, have abundant and cheap electricity, and preferably it should be close to an international airport. The machine has to be fairly horizontal so that the ground must be flat to within 20 metres over a substantial fraction of the area it occupies. The ground must also be stable, free from seismic disturbance, since the foundations of the machine must be firm enough to guarantee that misalignments stay within 0.15 mm (1 mm = 25th of an inch) over about 100 metres.[2] In the whole of Western Europe there are not many sites available that satisfy these stringent criteria. One hundred and forty possible situations have been investigated but only twelve have been found worth closer examination, and of these probably only three will be wholly suitable. Strong candidates are the Thetford area of Norfolk, England, the Ebersbergen Forest, near Munich, Germany, and the plain of Le Luc-Vidauban, Draguignan, France. Expense, in terms both of money and talent, is the chief reason why European countries have seen fit to collaborate on high energy particle research. The 300GeV machine will cost at least £140 million to build and will need 2500 PhD's to run it. But even if this were not the case, the dimensional and topographical needs of this particular technological operation would have made a joint effort advisable.

This is a vivid example but not an exceptional one. Exactly the same spatial problems arise in siting radio telescopes for example, especially with the cross-type variety. The original proposal for the Benelux Cross-Antenna Project was for a telescope with crossed arrays of aerials each 5 000 metres long (3 miles) – had it been implemented it would have required a surface area greater than the city of Leyden. Precisely the same demands arise over the location of international freight airports, deep-sea tanker ports, rocket launch complexes, the siting of nuclear power stations, desalination plants, tracking stations and so forth – all competing with each other and with other land uses for space in a compact, closely confined continent. It should be made clear that we are not considering here *environmental* planning – the optimum implementation of human establishments for gracious living conditions. Nor are we considering *economic* location for the best exploitation of resources, the best localization of production or the optimum employment of land. It is a question here of technological *lebensraum* – working-space needs of technical rules and modalities. Both environmental and economic planning in space at a European level would be a sensible, intelligent thing to do in our cramped quarters of the globe, but the failure to do so leads merely to inefficiency and inconvenience. For technological operations such planning is often a *necessary* condition for functioning at all.

In two cases, be it noted, the dimensions of modern technology have actually forced European countries to go right outside their own continent because there was literally no room. The testing of nuclear weapons is one case; here both Britain and France moved to the Pacific arena although France conducted her first series of tests in the empty spaces of the Sahara. The other case is for space research facilities. The territorial expanse required for space operations is immense. Complex 39 at Cape Kennedy, the launching-site for the Saturn v. programme, has three octagon launch pads each 3 000 ft across with 8 730 ft between each pad. The buildings alone are huge; the biggest in the world. The main manufacturing building of Mouchard operations, where the rocket is being made, occupies 43 acres, and the site's Vertical Assembly Building is 690 ft long, 513 ft wide, and 525 ft tall, with a further 170 ft below ground. It encloses 129 million cubic feet which compares to the 96 million cubic feet of the Great Pyramid of Cheops. There are a number of launch sites available in Europe for small-scale operations. *Esrange* at Kiruna, Sweden, within the Arctic Circle, is being built for sounding rockets of the *European Space Research Organization* (ESRO). The British use the Outer Hebrides and the French a 58 sq. mile site near Biscarosse; firings being made over the Bay of Biscay into the North Atlantic, with a tracking station in the Azores. But for large-scale space operations European countries have gone overseas. The French have been using the Hammaguir range in the Sahara for their Diamant rocket programme. The Italians have got over the spatial problem by using two sea-based launch platforms, the Santa Rita and the San Marco, which they towed to Formosa Bay, East Africa. Britain and her partners in the *European Space Vehicle Launcher Development Organization* (ELDO) use the Woomera range in Southern Australia. The prohibited area around Woomera is the size of England and Scotland, and the impact point, 1 100 nautical miles away to the north-west at Talgarno, is the same size as France. For certain types of operation equatorial launching sites are advantageous, and ELDO has accepted the French Government's invitation to use French Guiana where a $\frac{1}{4}$ million acre site on the coast has been put aside for the purpose.

One field where planning in the dimension of space is already pursued in Europe is the military sector. NATO has established what is called an infrastructure system – 'fixed' installations necessary for the effective operation and deployment of forces, all jointly paid for by members of the Alliance. The system incorporates 220 airfields, 5 000 miles of pipeline and 27 000 miles of telephone line and submarine cable. The heart of the pipeline network is the 3 000 mile Central European Pipeline (CEP) running from Dunkirk to Charmont and from Le Havre to Aachen and beyond; it includes 25 tanker terminal points, 250 bomb-proof pumping stations and 160 underground depots. The day to day running of the system is in the hands of national administrations and fuel moves unimpeded over frontiers, free from tax and customs charges. The Central European Operating Agency, a civilian body with responsibility to two separate committees – one military and one political, ensures that the network operates as an integrated, uniform system.

Another important piece of infrastructure is the common air-defence system between North Cape, Norway, and Turkey. This is keyed to an integrated telecommunications network with 6 000 circuits which transmits early radar warning of enemy ground and air attack to command positions. The speed of aircraft and missiles make an integrated system of this kind indispensable to the defence of countries in the NATO area.

A new, automated system – NATO *Air Defence Ground Environment* (NADGE), is under construction to cope with the enormously increased speeds of attacking aircraft. It will feed attack information direct to intercepting planes. It is significant that while General de Gaulle has withdrawn from the NATO command structure he remains determined to stay in the NADGE set-up; without this early warning system his *force de frappe*, for reasons of scale, would be less credible than it is.

NADGE is similar to the earlier established *Ballistic Missile Early Warning System* (BMEWS) – an ultra high speed radar which maintains watch on the Polar regions. With stations at Fylingdales, Yorkshire, Thule, Greenland, and Clear, Alaska, it provides Britain with 4 minutes warning and America with 15 minutes. At the USA's air-defence command at Colorado Springs, a trajectory of the missile's flight is fed into the missile / impact predictor which calculates the point of impact and the time remaining. BMEWS itself is not part of the infrastructure programme but serves for the defence of the whole Alliance just the same. The lay-out and siting of all these installations is planned, not on a national basis, but on a regional basis, according to geographical, strategic and technological criteria – because their effective operation requires it.

*

Technology therefore has its own dimensions, dimensions which bear little relation to political perimeters, and to comply with its rules and modalities nations have been compelled to cooperate. But if, as a result, Europe is today closely interlocked in a purely technical sense, little of this has percolated to the political level. We have a technically united community but a politically divided one. Indeed, in relation to its size, Western Europe remains the most fragmented area of the globe. Certainly, some concessions have been made to technology, but a pragmatic, functional, piecemeal approach has sufficed. We have not been obliged to alter our traditional political concepts, and technology has not led to the demise of the territorial state. We are still all very sovereign and independent – whatever that may mean in this situation. Nations are closer together but they are not more sociable and trusting. Far from it. It is a paradox of our century that at the moment when physical contact between nations has never been better, nationalism has never been more rampant and allegiance to international ideals never lower.

The word Nationalism describes the complicated cluster of feelings and emotions that instill a sense of cohesion and distinctiveness in people and sets them apart, in their own minds, from other groups. Language, race, geographical unity and continuity, shared historical experience, a common foe, parallel economic interests – are all factors which animate this consciousness. To catalogue and analyze them all would take us beyond the orbit of this book, but part of the blame for national entrenchment in our time is attributable to the new technology itself.

Communications media, after all, are neutral in themselves. They can be used constructively or destructively, but as they are used today they are often more divisive than integrative. There is no more effective instrument for creating goodwill between countries than wireless, yet throughout the world it is deliberately exploited for ideological propaganda and cultural imperialism – exacerbating world tensions. Millions of pounds are spent each year jamming these hostile transmissions even though this reduces the number of frequencies on the short band waves for which there are already more applications than can be met; and even though jamming is expressly contrary to Article 19 of the *Universal Declaration of Human Rights* which states that 'Everyone has the right of freedom of opinion and expression; this right includes freedom to hold opinions without interference and to seek, receive, and impart information and ideas through any media and regardless of frontiers.'

In Europe, before and during the Second World War, radio propaganda was a serious source of discord. Hitler used it freely to inflame German minorities against their host states and the Dollfuss Government was the first to use jamming in an attempt to prevent these attacks from being heard in Austria. But since the war radio has not been an important disruptive force in Western Europe itself – although it continues so along the cold war front both in Europe and the world at large.

Technical incompatiblity is another way in which the integrative qualities of communications can be effectively destroyed. The railway gauge dispute illustrates some of the difficulties this can cause for the movement of goods. In England the majority of railway companies adopted the standard 'narrow' gauge of 4 ft 8½ in, but Brunel, the chief engineer of the Great Western Railway, opted for the broad 7 ft gauge. Fortunately, Parliament intervened in 1846 to rule that all new lines must be built on the narrow gauge. Similarly in the United States it was left to the President to intervene in 1885 to regulate in favour of the narrow gauge. The International Convention of 1886 established 4 ft 8½ in as the standard throughout Europe with the exception of Russia, Spain and Ireland. It was the first really notable example of international standardization. In Australia, on the other hand, each state was allowed to set up its own standard. Some went for the narrow gauge, some for 3 ft 6 in, and some for 5 ft 3 in. It has taken years to sort out the mess and to this day railway track incompatibilities remain a major impediment to interstate trading. It is only in 1968 that all the state capitals are finally joined through a common gauge.

These technical divisions are often deliberately perpetuated for political and commercial reasons. We now have a classic example of this sort of idiocy in the failure of European governments to agree a common colour TV system. For international programme exchanges in colour TV by direct link or video tape recording the colour standard *and* the line standard must be the same. Where line standards differ in black and white (monocrome) a converter is available, but at the moment there is no line converter for colour systems and it will take several years to develop one. But where the line standard is the same then colour conversion between two colour systems is practicable by means of a transcoder;[3] but not without additional expense, not without some degradation in picture quality, not without a diversion of technical resources to solve the problem, and not without diminishing the market for colour sets. So a common colour system for Europe seemed sensible, and work began in 1962 to settle it. Both the EBU and the ITU went into the question. Three systems were considered; the NTSC system (American), the SECAM system (French) and the PAL system (German). Britain at first favoured the American system but later switch to PAL which the Netherlands, Switzerland, Italy and Germany already backed. The French, however, wanted their own system adopted and made an agreement with Russia and other East European countries to develop it. And there things have stuck; each nation anxious to recover its research costs and protect national industries from foreign competition. Thus PAL will have its 41 million viewers and SECAM its 25 million. For the time being the picture is further blurred by the fact that although there is general agreement to move toward a common line standard (625 lines) there are still five different line systems in use in Western Europe: the British 405 lines per picture, the Flemish-Belgium 625 lines, the German-Dutch Gerber system, the French-Belgium 819 lines and the French standard 819 lines. Whatever happens in Europe the Americans will continue with their NTSC system so at the very moment when satellites are on the point of providing us with world-wide TV, the monocrome division between the American 525 lines and the proposed European 625 lines is to be perpetuated in colour.

These technical divisions are a major economic hazard but they can hardly be considered as an important source of political cleavage in Europe. They may be used to further political and economic divisions but they are more a symptom than a cause of political ills, and in any case the colour TV dispute is an aberration from the general inclination of nations to collaborate in technical matters. It is a remarkable fact that during the Second World War the warring nations, while using jamming for tactical and piratical purposes, nevertheless continued to collaborate by registering their use of radio frequencies with the ITU.

ENTRENCHMENT OF THE STATE

Why then has it proved so difficult to adjust our economic and political organization to the dimensions of technology? Why are we so well integrated technically but so severely disintegrated organizationally? And anyway does it matter? That it matters is the object of this book to show, and the cause of this organizational lag can be traced to the fact that the technological revolution, besides broadening the area of our activities, has also incessantly multiplied them. The result is that our procedures and processes are infinitely more complicated and this has required an ever higher organization to control and direct it. Inevitably, the tendency has been for this authority to be exercised within the established organization of the nation-state, and the increasing speed with which the nation-states have increased their solidarity and integration has impeded the formation of organization at the international level. Thus existing political patterns and structures have been strengthened and solidified, giving rise to opposite tendencies of disintegration, differentiation and disorganization internationally, and world integration has been retarded.

The process of national consolidation at the expense of international integration is seen most clearly in the economic sector, where the position has been surveyed with some precision by the economist, Gunnar Myrdal.[4]

Prior to 1914, the partial world of the economically advanced countries was closely integrated in economic terms. It was possible to travel without passports and visas. Trade was virtually untrammelled by tariff and quota restrictions, and the factors of production, labour and capital, were free to move over national frontiers to where they might be most profitably employed. On the outbreak of the First World War this state of so-called 'normalcy' came to an end, and ever since the state has been enlarging its role in the economic life of all countries. The war effort compelled governments to take on new powers and responsibilities. After the war these powers of intervention were retained and new barriers to trade were raised to insulate national economies from the adverse influences of outside events. An uninterrupted series of international crises, especially the Great Depression, led to increasingly nationalistic economic policies as nations built up their armoury of policies to defend their welfare and stability. Trade became discriminatory. The movement of persons, merchandise and services, capital and enterprise were controlled and restricted. National economic integration was advanced at the cost of international economic integration. Thus as fast as natural barriers to trade were obliterated by new contact techniques, new, artificial barriers were erected to fragment the world market.

On the arrival of the Welfare State, with the government as a provider and equalizer of opportunity, the problem hardened. The state became still more protective and nationalistic as it pushed its way into every facet of economic activity not only to safeguard full-employment and stability but to redirect and speed economic development. Economies began to be managed, but always on a national basis since the international market is full of risks and hazards over which national administrations have no authority. Each step towards national integration led to further international economic disorder, and the resulting instability fed national autarky which further intensified international disintegration – 'the causation is circular and the process cumulative and bound to proceed further, unless it is redirected in a radical fashion.'

Such is the drift of Myrdal's argument, but the really vital point of his analysis is that this process does not only operate at the *economic level*; it produces an introversion of interests and by strengthening people's identification, solidarity and loyalty to the community it cements the psychological foundation of the nation-state. 'Organizations become increasingly directed towards winning material advances for their members; when the advances are procured, these are felt to have been earned by group solidarity. As they all operate within the national framework, this whole trend tends to turn people's interests inwards, towards the situations and problems at home, and to spread a defensive ideology of national group protectionism.' In this way the national boundary acquires new functions and takes on an increasing practical importance for everyone. This tends to lessen the experience, and weaken the feeling, of international solidarity. 'The nation-state and all that goes on within its framework becomes the practical reality for everybody, while internationalist strivings are unpractical dreams.'

Whatever the precise reason for the entrenchment of the territorial state in our day, the fact remains that the technology that has forcibly brought distant peoples into more frequent contact has not automatically provided the basis for wider international solidarity. The new techniques have established their own level of operations and eliminated the impermeability of states for good; but nationalism has not been transcended. Human solidarity is still confined within the boundaries of the nation-state. Reinhold Niebuhr has put the position in a nutshell, 'Our problem is that techniques have established a rudimentary world community but have not integrated it organically, morally or politically. They have created a community of mutual dependence but not of mutual trust and respect; without this higher integration advancing techniques tend to sharpen economic rivalries within a general framework of economic interdependence.'

Modern technology and our traditional political units and concepts are hopelessly misaligned.

Chapter III

The Quest for Space and Power

The movement to unite Europe is essentially a search for size consonant with the dimensions of modern technology, and an effort to achieve the necessary adjustments by peaceful means. It is a response to a challenge of scale. A reaction against the dwarfing of Europe in an age of giants in which continental-sized units have replaced nations as the effective components of international power. The Italians have coined a word for this adjustment to scale – *ridimensionamento*.[1] It is an attempt, in short, to bring the scale of political and economic organization to the level of techniques.

*

The idea of a 'United Europe' is not new. Under the Roman eagle it was a reality, and for a brief period, on a partial basis, it was a reality again in Charlemagne's empire of 800 AD. Even in the Middle Ages the Christian Commonwealth provided Europe with a 'unity of civilization'; although this did not take political form. And ever since Europe broke up into her mosaic of states a number of people have fancied themselves as rulers of a re-united Europe and set out to achieve their ambitions by force. Charles v. Philip ii, Louis xiv, Napoleon i, Wilhelm ii and Adolf Hitler all tried their hand. Napoleon saw himself, as he admitted, as the heir of Charlemagne, and Hitler and his 'new order' was but the latest attempt to unite Europe under the hegemony of one power. But as the Corsican lamented on

St Helena – Europe was not to be tamed by violence. The threat of predominance of one state was always fiercely and successfully contested. These schemes came to nothing and their perpetrators had an unenviable end. Charles v suffered a nervous breakdown and retired to a monastery where he passed the time of day rehearsing his funeral. Napoleon died in exile, poisoned, if we are to believe some stories, by the brutal British. And Herr Hitler did himself in. Submission to the political primary of one group was not, and is not, an acceptable basis for union between Europeans.

Besides resort to force there have also been attempts to accomplish unity by appeals to reason. Many plans were laid. Some, it must be admitted, were solely concerned with power and sought to advance national interest at others' expense by means more subtle, less brazen, than outright war. But most accepted Europe as she was, a 'unity in diversity' in which the nation states form the basic units. They were not concerned to fuse the nations into one structure but were intent on harmonizing them together, as separate entities, in a *systemè général*.

Behind this search there have been two persistent motives; one 'external', and one 'internal'. The aim of the first was to maintain the security and integrity of the European continent against some outside threat or menace – imaginary or real. Sometimes Russia, and sometimes even England was seen as the danger, but on most occasions the threat came from Islam where the struggle reached its climax in the crusading expeditions. The second motive found its *raison d'être* within Europe in the pursuit of 'perpetual peace'. Its sponsors strove to prevent Europe from tearing herself apart by continual war. It became a constant element in the search for unity from the 17th century onwards.

Pierre Dubois, a 14th century writer, was one of the earliest campaigners of the European cause. In his book, *De recuperatione Terrae Sancte*, he proposed a European Confederation which was to be ruled by a council of 'wise, expert and faithful men'. Dubois saw Europe's internicide struggles as the cause of the Turkish advance and wanted unity so that Europe's energies might be directed towards the recovery of the Holy Land. To ensure peace it was not enough to praise its benefits or even agree to keep it; war could only be prevented by suitable institutions. The recovery of the Holy Land for Christendom was also the pretext for the proposals Antoine Marigny put to the King of Bohemia in 1464. He wanted to emancipate peoples and kings by the organization of a 'new Europe' which was to have a diet and an assembly of Christian kings and princes. The 'Grand Design' of the Duc de Sully had similar aims. In his plan the Germans were to be re-united and an equipoise was to be kept by the division of Europe into fifteen states of more or less equal strength. Domestic peace was to be maintained by a European army. François de la Noue, and a Greek named Minotto, also formulated plans against the Turk, and at the beginning of the 17th century Liebnitz was advocating unity so that Europe might combine her forces to carry Christianity to the rest of the world.

The Turks besieged Vienna for the second and last time in 1682. They failed to take it. The Turkish movement had spent its force and with the removal of this danger proposals for European union were devoted primarily to the preservation of peace. It was the desire for general peace that inspired Émeric Crucé to propose an association of states with an assembly at which all the sovereigns were to have permanent ambassadors. Decisions were to be reached by majority voting and members were to collaborate in dealing with refractory states by pooling their armed forces. Peace too, was the prevailing objective in the international law writings of the Dutch jurist, Grotius. In *De jure belli et pacis*, he was the first to point to the need for conflicts to be settled by the arbitration of a power not a party to the dispute. William Penn wrote his *Essay towards the Present and Future Peace of Europe* in 1693. He advocated a united Europe with a parliament in which the votes were to be weighted according to the demographic and economic circumstances of the member states. Decisions were to be enforced, if need be, by a European army paid for by the wrongdoer.

The Abbé de Saint Pierre made a similar appeal in his *Mémoires pour rendre la paix perpétuelle en Europe* (1717). He wanted a perpetual alliance between European sovereigns. Their dealings were to be vetted by a European senate and backed by collective sanctions. The pact was to be jointly financed and subject to revision by majority voting, except for fundamental issues where unanimity was necessary. Peace was also the concern of the Comte de Saint-Simon. His 'new Europe' was to have England and France as its cornerstone. Auguste Comte called for a 'Western Republic' consisting of five great powers, France, Germany, Italy, Spain and England, with various associated states. Bentham, Kant, Considérant, Hugo, Mazzini, Cobden and Proudhon, all made proposals in the interests of peace; and there were many more besides.

Each and everyone of them came to nothing. The interest shown in peace fluctuated throughout history. It was most intense, naturally enough, during and immediately after a major war. But memories fade swiftly. What one generation learnt to its cost, the next had to learn over again. The Romans used to say that 'wise men learn by other men's mistakes; fools, by their own'. But this wisdom was not heeded and peace never provided a sense of common interest for very long. The diversity of Europe proved stronger than her unity and war returned time and again to plague her citizens. To most people these proposals for perpetual peace were quite unrealistic – 'high sounding nothings' to use Metternich's contemptuous phrase of Tsar Alexander's mystical Holy Alliance. The 'balance of power' was the best system that statesmen could devise to preserve peace and stability – a precarious concept creating the bare semblance of co-existence.

The brief periods when Europe did realize some solidarity was when there was something to unite against. Geoffrey Barraclough, has termed this 'a negative conception of unity'[2] directed against an outside enemy – a response to extra-European pressures. 'It was easier' he says 'to create a sense of unity on the basis of hostility and opposition than in view of the positive benefits it might confer. The Church might preach the brotherhood of Christians, but in vain; it was only when they united against Islam that they could act together, and then only so long as they felt the threat seriously.' External danger was the only element to provide a common interest strong enough to override national differences. The trouble was that for so many centuries Europe enjoyed such an unassailable position of supremacy that she was not seriously threatened from outside. The external pressures making for closer unity were absent.

The present-day movement for European integration gains strength and momentum directly from the fact that for the first time in three hundred years Europe is once more threatened from without. Not that there is any immediate or overt peril – although the Red Army did provide, or was thought to provide, such a danger in the late 1940's. The threat arises from the conditions of the modern world in which technology equates power more closely with physical size. Europe has lost her political primacy because she has been dwarfed and overtaken by the world powers of continental proportions on her flanks. So long as her strength is wasted and dissipated by national divisions, her power, influence, wealth and prestige are in jeopardy. In an age of global politics and civilization parochial rivalries and antagonisms have not been eliminated but they do seem less relevant. In this wider perspective Europeans have found something to unite against and have begun to discover a sense of identity *as Europeans*.

This is not to say that peace has not been an important motive in the quest for unity since the war. On the contrary, it has. The *Schuman Declaration* of May, 1950, which was the starting point for European integration as distinct from mere cooperation, proposed the pooling of French and German coal and steel resources under a common authority. At the time this idea was valued less for its economic advantages than as a means of bringing the Ruhr permanently under supranational control and thus neutralizing it as an arsenal in war.

E

The aim of unity here was primarily as a means to peace. The Declaration itself makes this quite clear: – 'The contribution which an organized and living Europe can bring to civilization is indispensable to the maintenance of peaceful relations. In taking upon herself for more than twenty years the role of champion of a united Europe, France has always had as her essential aim the service of peace . . .'. It was felt that the solidarity in production which would be established under such an authority would make it plain that any war between France and Germany would be '. . . not merely unthinkable, but materially impossible.'

But unceasing peace does not ensue merely because tired men are determined that there shall be no more war. Of course peace was a powerful inducement for Europeans to get together after the war, but there is no cause to think that the general revulsion with militarism, the yearning for peace, and all the resolutions that this sort of thing would never be allowed to happen again, provided any firmer foundation for unity after the Second World War than after the 'war to end all wars' or the Thirty Year War. Europeans identify themselves as Europeans in the perspective of a wider world; a perspective which did not exist before the revolution in communications converted the world into a single system. Without this fundamental change in scale evoked by the new technology the ideal of European unity could not have progressed from an idle speculation to maturing reality within twenty years of a great internal war. For the varied national groups in Europe the most relevant argument for banding together is that this is the only way that they can hope to return to some influence in the world. The foreign ministers of the Six, who assembled at Messina in 1955 to discuss setting up a common market, declared such a policy 'indispensable if Europe is to maintain her position in the world, regain her influence and prestige and achieve a continuing increase in the standard of living of her population.' As in the past then, the internal reorganization of Europe is advocated in terms of a hard external reality, but unlike the past the situation creating this threat is a permanent state of affairs, and thus helps to guarantee the attainment of a more abiding community than any before.

*

A knowledge of geography and an appreciation of the dependence of political events on the physical character of the earth has never been a strong point of our leaders. But if they have had little geopolitical sense, they have had even less understanding of the consequences of technological progress and its impact on the international scene. The cost of their neglect and ignorance has been the failure of this country to grasp the true dimensions of the modern world and to find for ourselves a place within it.

The new navigation techniques perfected by the end of the 15th century gave world-wide mobility to the Europeans and opened up the globe for discovery and exploitation. As we have seen, in those days civilization was confined to the rimlands beside coastlines and river systems. Travel and the conveyance of goods were borne on the all-embracing unity of the seas. It was a seaman's age and sea-power was the key to world primacy. For a time the arrival of the steamship confirmed this position, for while the sea is a ready-made highway, railroads take time and money to build. Throughout the last century Britain's undisputed control of the oceans ensured her position of world supremacy. This situation lasted until about the 1880's when the use of efficient surface transport enabled the development of land areas and led to the emergence of land scale powers. It was the end of the maritime world created during the Age of Discovery.

America and Russia grew spontaneously under the impact of these changes. In 1800 four-fifths of the American population lay fringed along the Atlantic sea-board. At this time the United States embraced some eight hundred thousand square miles, organized on a loose federal basis. Internal development was hindered by slow and costly transportation and inland settlements were economically detached. But by 1850 the population was sprawled over almost three million square miles and the vast spaces of the American Middle West had been tamed and occupied. The ease of new communications made it possible for the United States to sustain this unity on a scale hitherto impossible. A similar movement occurred in Russia. In the two hundred years after 1560 she grew five-fold in size and today embraces almost eight and a half million square miles. In this case it was only with the coming of air transport that Russia has been able to complete the consolidation of this huge territorial spread. But whereas Russia and America were free to expand into largely empty spaces, geographically contiguous to them, uninhibited expansion within the long settled, congested lands of Europe was impossible. The only areas for European growth were overseas. Vast holdings were acquired and Britain got the lion's share. But although these empires still exist as the British Commonwealth and the French Community they provide no real power base, for in this case it has proved impossible to assimilate and consolidate the many alien races of these diffuse, and tenuously controlled, maritime groups. And so America and Russia have reached the dimensions appropriate to the 20th century but Europe is still netted to the boundaries drawn in the coach and horse era.

FOREWARNINGS

The significance of these developments was lost on our leaders; or if it was not then no action was taken to meet the fundamental change in the geographical bases of world power. From the advantage of our hindsight it may seem unjust to judge 19th century statesmen for their failure to comprehend the revolution in their midst. The pace of progress was furious and the geopolitical changes produced by this fast development are still in the making. There were, nevertheless, a few intelligent, well informed men who foresaw and forewarned of the shape of things to come.

To the historian, J. R. Seeley, lecturing in the 1880's, it was already apparent that the future lay with those 'enormous political aggregates' America and Russia. He predicted that in the 20th century they would 'surpass in power the states now called great, as much as the great country-states of the 16th century surpassed Florence.' Unlike most of his contemporaries Seeley had a firm grasp of the political consequences of the new contact techniques. 'Perhaps we are hardly alive to the vast results which are flowing in politics from modern mechanism. Throughout the greater part of human history the process of state-building has been governed by the strict conditions of space. For a long time no high organization was possible except in very small states. In antiquity the good states were usually cities.... In medieval Europe, states sprang up which were on a larger scale ... but through the invention of the representative system these states have risen to a higher level. We now see states with vivid political consciousness on territories of two hundred thousand square miles and in populations of thirty millions. A further advance is now being made. The federal system has been added to the representative system, and at the same time steam and electricity have been introduced. From these improvements has resulted the possibility of highly organized states on a yet larger scale.'

Seeley believed that there were two alternatives before Britain. Either she could disband her Empire, in which case she would rank no higher than other European states; or she could bind the dominions into a federal union, in which case she could stand with America and Russia in the first rank of powers – measured in population and area. He rejected the 'Little England' approach and appealed for 'Greater Britain'. The Empire was not like the old type of empire founded by force – 'congeries of nations forced together by a conquering horde'. It was a real community. An extension of the English race into other lands bound together by nationality, language and religion. By this he meant the Anglo-Saxon dominions. He excluded India as 'an alien race and religion, bound to us only by the tie of conquest'. Greater Britain was necessary because in the world of tomorrow bigness meant greatness and power. '... the question, whether large states or small states are best, is not one which can be answered or ought to be discussed absolutely. We often hear abstract panegyrics upon the happiness of small states. But observe that a small state among small states is one thing and a small state among large states quite another. Nothing is more delightful than to read of the bright days of Athens and Florence, but those bright days lasted only so long as the states with which Athens and Florence had to do were states on a similar scale of magnitude. Both states sank at once as soon as large country-states of consolidated strength grew up in their neighbourhood. The lustre of Athens grew pale as soon as Macedonia rose, and Charles v speedily brought to an end the great days of Florence. Now if it be true that a larger type of state than any hitherto known is springing up in the world, is this not a serious consideration for those states which rise only to the old level of magnitude?'[3]

The theme of imperial consolidated was taken up by men like Cecil Rhodes and Joseph Chamberlain in the heyday of imperialism at the turn of the century. It is forever propagated by Beaverbrook's *Daily Express*, but it has been rejected by Island and Dominions alike.

The future ordering of political events was also anticipated by the geopoliticians of the last century, although they were not agreed as to the strategic consequences of the new technology, and all tended to neglect or underestimate the implications of continuing technological progress. Geopolitics is the art of understanding the opportunities and limitations of geography in international affairs, and the job of its students is to provide us with hypotheses with which to explain the past and predict the future. The American admiral, Alfred Mahan, and the British geographer, Sir Halford Mackinder, both formulated their theories on the lay out and configuration of land and sea. Mahan, writing in the 1890's,[4] was convinced that the unbroken continuity of the oceans, the configuration of coastlines, and the comparative advantage of movement by sea over transport by land, meant that sea-power would remain the key to world political supremacy. The seas formed a single body of water enveloping every continent and island whereas overland routes ended at the coasts. He doubted if a mainland state sharing a continent with other powerful states could ever command the sea in the way an island power could. Since Britain was an island and had control of the narrow seaways vital to ocean-borne traffic, the Dover Straits, the Straits of Malacca, Gibraltar and Suez and the southern opening to the Red Sea, she would continue to dominate for a long time to come. In Mahan's view, the only country in the world with the potential to supersede Britain was the United States. She also had the advantage of insularity and possessed, besides, the resources of a whole continent.

Although Mahan lived in the midst of the Railway Age and beheld the coming of the car and the aeroplane, he did not attempt to explore their repercussions on his theory. He overlooked the possibility that islands might be bombed from the air. He did not foresee that air power would render narrow seaways and inland seas untenable to shipping in war. Sea power, he maintained, would retain its singular importance because the transit of goods in large quantities and for great distances was decisively more easy and copious by sea than by land. To some extent this is true even today. Water transport for goods in bulk is generally cheaper, and the costs of transport overland often makes water a more important connecting link than land. But shipping transport is clearly not as vital as it was in Mahan's day. In the exchange of information and the movement of persons, air transport, which rides with equal facility over land and sea, has evened things up for the land and the development of large freight planes will reduce the superiority of ocean-borne traffic still further.

Towards the end of his life Mahan began to waver in his conviction on the absolute superiority of sea-power – '... unless we succeed in exploiting the air, water remains the great medium of transportation'. However, his doctrine was accepted as a dogma of universal validity. It was quoted in support of the naval armaments race between Germany, Britain and the United States in which the Royal Navy was forced to abandon its traditional 'two-power standard' – superiority in capital ships over the pooled strength of the next two largest navies. By 1906 the US Navy had become the second largest in the world and Britain tacitly accepted a policy of not reckoning on the possibility of hostilities with America. In the *Treaty of Washington* of 1921 Britain went further and accepted the principle of Anglo-American parity in carriers and capital ships. By 1950 the US Navy had not only overtaken the Royal Navy in strength, but was equal to all the major navies of the world combined. So in this respect Mahan had been right. America possessed the resources of a whole continent.

Mackinder presented his celebrated 'heartland' thesis before the Royal Geographical Society in 1904.[5] He started with the same premise as Mahan; that dominant naval power was the key. But Mackinder attached greater weight to the development of overland transport and reached different conclusions. For him the configurations of land and sea pointed not to the primacy of island states but to the emergence of a globally dominant empire located in the 'heartland' – the regions of the Arctic and continental drainage in the Eurasian landmass. His lecture was meant to serve as a warning to Britain of the danger of Germany getting control of this area.

Mackinder saw the world as nine-twelfths sea and three-twelfths land and he divided the land into the 'world-island' – the Europe-Asia-Africa landmass, and a series of smaller, off-shore islands – the Americas and Australia He also saw history as a basic struggle for domination between continental and maritime nations. The inventions of the Age of Discovery gave mobility to the people of the marginal lands of the world and increased the importance of sea-power relative to land-power. But now the railway made possible the effective integration of wide land areas, allowed land based states to recapture the mobility they had enjoyed in the days of the horsemen, and had set in motion a process that would lead to the displacement of sea-power by land-power. Sea-power could only dominate the edges of landmasses, not the interiors of large continents.

The heartland had all the requisites of world empire – vast continental resources and ports on every ocean. But the area also derived importance from its natural security and median position on the world-island. It was endowed by nature with remarkable defensive strength. To the north, the Arctic Sea, frozen all the year round, made the area unapproachable by sea, and to the south and east there were mountain chains and vast desert-steppe plateaus. It was a perfect citadel for defence and a secure base for offensive operations against the rest of the world-island. This situation gave the people who could control the heartland the chance to win out over the people of the 'outer crescent' lands.

The Eastern European Plain was the one direction from which this citadel was pregnable, and in 1904, even though Russia was owner-occupier of the area, it was Germany, in Mackinder's opinion, who was in a better position to gain control of it than any other power. This was still his position in *Democratic Ideals and Reality*, published in 1919, in which he elaborated on his thesis and in which his famous dictum – 'Who rules East Europe commands the Heartland; Who rules the Heartland commands the World-Island; Who rules the World-Island commands the World.' was annunciated. It was only in the 1940's that Mackinder acknowledged that the industrial development of Russia made her powerful enough to keep control of the area, and he pointed to her rise.

Thus in its original conception Mackinder's theory was primarily concerned with *location* and only incidentally with *size*. The heartland was the 'pivot area' of the world-island and out of reach of hostile powers. Whether so much can be read into geographical phenomena is doubtful, but in any case the validity of the theory depended on the conditions of the day and the security and seclusion this afforded the heartland. Technological progress since then has eroded the foundation of the theory. The heartland is no more safe today than any other surface configuration so far as its location is concerned, and in an age of rockets and nuclear bombs it is perhaps time to abandon hypotheses based on geophysical features and their location.

Mackinder himself claimed that his strategic concept had

lost none of its significance in the conditions of modern warfare. In 1943 he wrote, ' . . . the conclusion is unavoidable that if the Soviet Union emerges from this war as conqueror of Germany, she must rank as the greatest land Power on the globe. Moreover, she will be the Power in the strategically strongest defensive position. The Heartland is the greatest natural fortress on earth. For the first time in history it is manned by a garrison sufficient both in number and in quality.'[6] But Mackinder had in fact shifted his ground. The emphasis now was less on location than on size. Russia had twenty times the area of France and here was space sufficient for defence in depth and for strategic retreat. Now it was the invulnerable hugeness of Russia that gave the area its strength, for Mackinder saw, rightly, that while the value of any strategic location had been diminished by technological progress, sheer spaciousness had lost none of its importance. Indeed technology accentuates the strategic advantage of large, contiguous areas for in the conditions of modern warfare space strengthens defensive as it weakens offensive operations.

It was the conservative politician, L. S. Amery, in a brief reply at the close of Mackinder's 1904 lecture, who indicated the potential weakness of the thesis and put forward an alternative hypothesis of his own. '. . . both the sea and the railway are going in the future . . . to be supplemented by air as a means of locomotion, and when we come to that . . . a great deal of this geographical distribution must lose its importance, and the successful powers will be those who have the greatest industrial basis. It will not matter whether they are in the centre of a continent or on an island; those people who have the industrial power and *the power of invention and science* will be able to defeat all others.'[7] This is an idea to which it will be necessary to return.

Yet surely, the most remarkable prophecy of all was that of the French aristocrat, Alexis de Tocqueville. In *Democracy in America*, first published in 1835, right at the beginning of the revolution in communications, he outlined with almost uncanny prescience the future for his readers. His vision is worth quoting at some length. 'The Middle Ages were a period when everything was broken up; when each people, each province, each city, and each family, had a strong tendency to maintain its distinct individuality. At the present time an opposite tendency seems to prevail, and the nations seem to be advancing to unity. Our means of intellectual intercourse unite the most remote parts of the earth; and it is impossible for men to remain strangers to each other, or to be ignorant of the events which are taking place in any corner of the globe. The consequence is that there is less difference, at the present day, between the Europeans and their descendants in the New World, in spite of the ocean which divides them, than there was between certain towns in the 13th century, which were separated only by a river. If this tendency to assimilation brings foreign nations closer to each other, it must *a fortiori* prevent the descendants of the same people from becoming aliens to each other.

'The time will therefore come when one hundred and fifty millions of men will be living in North America, equal in condition, the progeny of one race, owing their origin to the same cause, and preserving the same civilization, the same language, the same religion, the same habits, the same manners, and imbued with the same opinions, propagated under the same forms. The rest is uncertain, but this is certain; and it is a fact new to the world – a fact fraught with such portentous consequences as to baffle the efforts even of the imagination.'

De Tocqueville went on to surmise, 'There are, at the present time, two great nations in the world, which seem to tend towards the same end, although they started from different points. I allude to the Russians and the Americans. Both of them have grown up unnoticed; and whilst the attention of mankind was directed elsewhere, they have suddenly assumed a most prominent place amongst the nations; and the world learned their existence and their greatness at almost the same time.

'All other nations seem to have nearly reached their natural limits and only to be charged with the maintenance of their power; but these are still in the act of growth: all the others have stopped, or continue to advance with extreme difficulty; these are proceeding with ease and celerity along a path to which the human eye can assign no term.... Their starting-point is different, and their courses are not the same; yet each of them seems to be marked out by the will of Heaven to sway the destinies of half the globe.'[8]

ASCENDENCY LOST

Whether it was by the will of Heaven or not, by 1919 it was no longer possible for European statesmen to evade the compelling logic of the new technology. The era in which Europe had been the political and economic centre of the globe was definitely at an end. Some concessions had to be made to the new bases of power politics, and for the first time our leaders began to look seriously at proposals for unity.

The campaign was led by Count Coudenhove-Kalergi.[9] Europe, he said, had lost her ascendancy and from her dominating position she had been thrown back on the defensive. She had forfeited her world-wide hegemony because her peoples were disunited and she would forfeit her independence and what remained of her prosperity if the disunion continued. 'If the science of politics fails to adapt itself to the science of communications, the resulting tensions will inevitably lead to terrible catastrophes. The spatio-temporal *rapprochement* of neighbouring peoples must be followed by a political *rapprochement*, if conflicts are to be avoided.' The individual states had become too small to be able to lead an independent existence. Europe was in danger of becoming, politically and militarily, 'the chessboard of the world – a pawn in the hands of world politics, as once she was the arbiter.' The cause of the decline was not biological but political. 'Europe is not dying of old age, but because its inhabitants are killing and destroying one another with the instruments of modern science.... The peoples of Europe are not senile; it is only their political system that is senile.' Everybody discussed European questions, but nobody The European Question – 'Can Europe, so long as its political and economic division lasts, maintain its peace and independence with respect to the growing World Powers: or is it bound, in order to preserve its existence, to organize itself into a federal union?' '... whether Europe will be a union of states or a collection of ruins' depended on the answer to that question. 'Unite or disappear!' this was the inexorable dilemma for Europe.

The cause was taken up by Aristide Briand and when he became President of the Council in France he had the founding of a United States of Europe in his programme. Another French statesman, Édouard Herriot, wrote a book on the subject. 'We are proposing' he said 'to discipline a continent which in the course of centuries has dissipated a large part of its vital energies in wars which really amounted to civil wars.'[10] The emphasis here, was still on internal peace, and internicide struggles were seen as the chief cause of Europe's decline. Save for a small band of economists who saw that no European state by itself was now large enough to be an economic state of world standing, the need for size was still imperfectly felt.

In the event these proposals failed as others had before them. They failed primarily for two reasons. First, throughout the inter-war years European nations remained pre-eminent in world affairs and felt no threat to their position because the consequences of the new technology were hidden by the absence of the two world-powers from the international scene. Russia, by the Revolution, was alienated from the comity of nations and became preoccupied with her internal problems; the result of five centuries of misrule. America, on the other hand, returned to her traditional policy of isolation. She shut herself up in her continent, and there she stayed throughout the inter-war years, insulated, so she believed, from the cares of the world and apparently oblivious of the fact that technological progress was undermining the geographical basis for such a policy – a fact she learnt to her cost at Pearl Harbour. So European nations were left to play things out between themselves and felt no real threat to their position.

The proposals for union at this time also failed to find acceptance because the Germans understood only too well the necessity for scale in the modern world, and with them it became an obsession. Instead of using it as an argument in favour of European unity, they converted it into the 'sick' doctrine which justified the augmentation of Germany at the expense of other nations. Their instinct for size was correct; their method of achieving it reactionary and evil.

Germany had grown to unity under the impact of the new technology. Emerging as a great power late in the day, and with only a narrow outlet to the open sea, she was deprived of her place in the sun in which more fortunate nations basked. Her leaders developed claustrophobia – a morbid dread of confined spaces. They were, they claimed, a 'people without space' (Volk ohne Raum) and looked around for some place to grow.

Karl Hauschofer, who headed the *Institut für Geopolitik* in Munich between the wars, evolved a venomous theory on space which made growth in size look scientific and even irresistible. The state, he said, was an organism, endowed with both life and will. It must expand or pay the penalty of decay and disintegration for only 'a large space maintains life'. Life was thus a struggle between dynamic and stagnant nations for the redistribution of the earth. It was an irrefutable law of history that the strong devoured the weak.

This amazing contribution to political thought borrowed from the ideas of earlier thinkers; notably those of Friedrich Ratzel. Ratzel had made a study of 'space-conquering forces' and had laid out seven laws governing spatial growth. Every people had to be educated up from smaller to larger space conceptions, for a people's attitude to space was the touchstone of its capacity for survival and the decline of every state was attributable to a declining space consciousness of its people.

Hitler was certainly influenced by these ideas. In *Mein Kampf* he wrote, 'The size of a people's living area includes an essential factor for the determination of its outward security. The greater the amount of room a people has at its disposal, the greater is also its natural protection; because military victories over nations crowded in small territories have always been reached more effectively and more completely, than in the case of states which are territorially greater in size.' Germany fell short of the optimum and more *lebensraum* was needed as a source of nourishment. But this was not to be found in overseas colonies as the Kaiser had wanted, but in the winning of new soil and territory in *Mitteleuropa* (Central Europe) – an expansion in the European territory of the homeland. Only declining states sought stable frontiers. The first aim of the territorial policy of the future was '. . . to establish between the number and growth of population, on the one hand, and the size and value of the soil and territory, on the other hand, a viable, natural relationship.' And this aim was worth an 'investment in blood'.

And so all Germany became an armed camp and her state frontiers but a temporary halt of a nation on the march towards world domination. And off we went to war once more.

INDEPENDENCE THREATENED

It was clear, even before the end of hostilities, that Europe had now not only lost her ascendancy but that her independence was also threatened. As had been feared, she was becoming, if she had not already become, a pawn in the hands of world politics. Europeans saw their land swamped by the armies of external powers, albeit as liberators, who then proceeded to settle the post-war shape of Europe without a European voice at the conference table. Half Europe fell under the hegemony of Russia and the preservation of her remaining liberties was in the hands of the Americans. It was a favourable moment for those who wished to unite what was left of Europe. Nationalism, which had been strengthened in the First World War, and by fascism and economic nationalism between the wars, had been undermined by the militarism to which it gave effect. The nation-state itself had been discredited, first by its rapid and total collapse against the Nazi onslaught, and now by its failure to deal with the problems of reconstruction without the massive and generous aid the Americans supplied

under the Marshall Plan. Now the full consequences of technology and growing interdependence were felt, and it was seen
that the nations of the old scale of magnitude were becoming
as outmoded as the *Kleinstaaterie* of Germany had been in
the previous century. And so, at last, the quest for unity became
synonymous with the search for size consonant with the dimensions of modern techniques.

The European movement was immediately divided into two
camps. There were those who believed that the new standards
of size could be met through simple collaboration between
sovereign states – the functionalists; and there were those who
understood more perfectly the imperatives of the age and saw
that it was necessary to proceed further, pool sovereignties, and
organize Europe on a continental basis – the federalists.

The 'sector approach' was the initial strategy adopted by the
federalists. This was seen, not as a series of isolated steps, but
as a cumulative process. Behind the idea lay the 'spill-over'
concept – that action in one sphere would *necessitate* action
in another. Each sector, being 'inherently expansive', would
help to enforce a progressive integration, with political union
as the climax. At least, this was the idea. The *Schuman Declaration* outlined the plan, 'Europe will not be made all at once,
or according to a single, general plan. It will be built through
concrete achievements, which first create a *de facto* solidarity.
. . . In this way there will be realized, simply and speedily,
that fusion of interests which is indispensable to the establishment of an economic community; and that will be the germ
from which may grow a broader and deeper community between countries long opposed to one another by bloody
conflicts.'

Coal and steel were the first sectors to be integrated under
the *Treaty of Paris* which set up the *European Coal and Steel
Community* (ECSC) in 1951; atomic energy was the second
under the *Treaty of the European Atomic Energy Community*
(EURATOM) in 1958. Between these two treaties there were
several other proposals, including a 'Green Pool' for agriculture, a 'White Pool' for health, and a European Transport

Authority; none of which were realized. But the most important of these proposals was the *European Defence Community* (EDC). The cold war reached its height in the Korean War in 1950, and the Americans became convinced that it was necessary to rearm Germany. Five years after the German surrender this was hard for Europeans to swallow and to make it more palatable the Defence Community was proposed. There was to be a multinational army under European command in which German contingents were to be integrated. The federalists seized on the idea as an opportunity for effecting political unity, for the project amounted to an explicit merger of national sovereignties. They were too optimistic. This direct foray into the higher realms of sovereign susceptibilities proved premature. The French National Assembly rejected it and the project came to grief.

With the collapse of the EDC this period of 'creative opportunism' came to an end and the sector approach, with the exception of the atomic pool, was abandoned. The signing of the *Treaty of Rome* in March 1957, marked a more comprehensive approach to integration, embracing a number of sectors in the economic sphere.

*

In economics the size of the market is important because it helps to determine the structure of industry and the pace of economic development. As Adam Smith himself put it 'The division of labour is limited by the extent of the market'. One factor in the past which limited the extent of the market was the state of transportation and communications; but as the bounds of time and place have been shattered by new contact techniques so the size of the market has been constantly enlarged. Another factor limiting the market is the boundary of the nation-state which represents discontinuities to economic activity. Some of these discontinuities spring from real differences which follow national boundaries through variations in taste and culture. The importance of these too, as barriers to trade, have been reduced, although not eliminated, as the isolating

F

influence of geography has been abolished. Thus in the days of free trading in the last quarter of the 19th century the world provided a single market and all the economic space that was necessary. The concept of the nation from an economic standpoint was of little importance.

But as we have seen, in our own century the state has acquired increasing economic importance. Artificial discontinuities to economic operations have been erected at the state frontier. And thus with restrictions on international trade limiting the extent of the market, the quality of access to a market becomes important, and the idea of a definite geographical area within which there are equal conditions of trade becomes of great consequence in economic affairs.

The Common Market, which was established by the Treaty of Rome, seeks simply to provide greater economic space than is supplied within the economic frontiers of the state, by combining the separate national markets of member states into one single home market of continental size. It will achieve this not merely by removing tariffs and quantitative restrictions between participating countries – as in a free trade area, but also by equalizing tariffs in trade with non-member countries – as in a customs union. And it goes further than this. Besides removing restrictions on commodity movements within the union it also abolishes restrictions on factor movements – labour and capital, and seeks to harmonize national economic policies in so far as the disparities in these policies produce discrimination.

One of the first political economists to recognize the importance of 'space' for economic progress was Friedrich Lizt. He spent some time in the United States where he gained an appreciation of some of the advantages of a continental superstate held together in a single tariff unit under a federal government, with mass production based on a diversity of natural resources. In his native Germany the thirty-five states of the Germanic Confederation each had their own customs system and produced 'much the same effect as ligatures which prevent the free circulation of the blood.' The position was much the same in Italy. Between Milan and Florence, for instance, there were at one time eight customs houses and transit dues had to be paid across them all. On his return to Germany, Lizt was active in trying to bring order from chaos by uniting Germany economically within a customs union. Prussia produced the catalyst for change by setting up a single tariff for her territories in 1818. By 1828 most of Germany was grouped in three customs unions, the Prussian, the South German, and the Middle German Commercial Union, and in 1834 eighteen states united to form the *Zollverein* under Prussian leadership.

There was also a proposal in the last century for a central German customs union including the Hapsburg dominions, and this idea was revived in 1915 by Friedrich Naumann in his influential book *Mitteleuropa*. He advocated an Austro-German customs union because in his view '. . . no European nation, not even the German, by itself is large enough for an economic state of world standing. . . . This economic state has its customs frontiers just as the military state has its trenches. Within these frontiers it tries to create a universally active exchange area . . .'.

The idea was then taken by the German geopoliticians and carried to its extreme conclusion – complete economic self-sufficiency. *Grossraum Wirtschaft* became a central part of their space theory. Quite apart from strategic considerations, it was economically desirable for Germany to withdraw from the unstable world market into a viable economy large enough to contain its own essential supplies and to provide its own market. Otherwise Germany's means of life were completely outside her control and her industry at the mercy of world trade winds.

The Germans had a chance to try out their *Grossraum* policy in the occupied territories during the war, and to this day autarkic ideas linger on in some circles. The idea of a Eurafrican Union, in which Africa is seen as the resource-base for Europe in the same way as Canada is for the United States and Siberia for Russia, is one example.[11]

The value of the Common Market for the federalists in post-war Europe did not rest solely on the economic advantages of scale. Its political potential was also valuable. Again, the *Zollverein* was the inspiration and model. History showed that economic and political union were interdependent. With the political union of England and Scotland went economic union. Similarly with Ireland in 1826. In the United States the constitution of 1781 was purely political. The constitution of 1787, however, included economic union; it was one of the chief reasons for writing a new constitution. This pattern holds true for France, Italy, Canada, Australia and Switzerland. Economic and political union went hand in hand. Indeed, a proposal for a customs union between Belgium and France in the 1840's was vetoed precisely because it would compromise Belgium's political neutrality. The same argument is deployed by Russia today against Austria's accession to the Common Market. Political union without economic union is impractical and vice versa.

The *Zollverein* was the one case where a customs union preceded political union. It was not a consequence of political union but the means chosen to attain the desired political end. It occurred to the federalists that the Common Market might be used in the same way. Their conviction was supported by several reports on the subject. A League of Nations study had put it: 'For a customs union to exist, it is necessary to allow free movement of goods within the union. For a customs union to be a reality it is necessary to allow free movement of persons. For a customs union to be stable it is necessary to maintain free exchangeability of currency and stable exchange rates within the union. This implies, *inter alia*, free movement of capital within the union. When there is free movement of goods, persons, and capital in any area, diverse economic policies concerned with maintaining economic activity cannot be pursued. To assure uniformity of policy, some political mechanism is required. The greater the interference of the state in economic life, the greater must be the political integration within a customs union.'[12] Here then was a mechanism leading directly to political integration. For a common market to be complete it must be capped by political union. As one commentator has argued, to obtain the economic advantages of size free trade is no longer enough, what has to be integrated is '. . . the part hitherto played by national governments in setting the conditions – holding the ring, or even weighting the odds – which determine the economic activities of private citizens, labour, capital, business and industry'[13] – essentially a political exercise.

In attempting to create a common market strong pressures are automatically generated for poltical unity. And this was the target of the federalists.

THE BRITISH PREDICAMENT

From all these developments Britain excluded herself. When the Six wanted a common market, Britain wanted a free-trade area, and when the Six wanted supranational institutions with the pooling of sovereignties, Britain wanted the traditional intergovernmental conference with no surrender of political independence. Why have we been so reluctant to join in? The war had a good deal to do with it. Our experience was altogether dissimilar to that of the Six. We emerged structurally weakened but spiritually elated. There we were, one of the Big Three – an honour awarded us more for valour than for strength, in the know about nuclear weapons and with enormous prestige abroad. The upheavals of 1940, far from disillusioning us with the nation-state, had vindicated it for us. We were victorious and the nation of triumph. Our wartime role served merely to lengthen our self-deception on the realities of power, and the truth, so swiftly revealed to Europeans on the continent, escaped us.

The war also brought distrust with Europe and strengthened at the same time our friendship and confidence with the Americans. The Channel became wider than the Atlantic. And this partnership with America was further cemented by the necessity for a joint exercise of world responsibilities while Britain was dismantling her Empire.

Another factor after the war which strengthened nationalism was the introduction of the Welfare State and other measures of economic nationalism. Socialism is devoted to international ideals and brotherhood, but in practice it develops national exclusiveness. 'There is nothing socialists nationalize so well as socialism' Ignazio Silone once expressed it.

And then there was the Empire to impair our sense of reality and make an accurate appraisal of our position more difficult. Formerly this provided us with the space and power to rank us with the greatest. It gave us political control over our means of life – raw materials and food, and after the breakup of the international economy continued to supply us with the market dimensions modern production requires. As Seeley had mentioned, unlike other European empires, a great part of the British Empire was not held together by force. Those spaces which were largely empty when conquered were settled by a vast migration of British people, and to this day they form a genuine community, with political substance or not, preserving, as they do, the same civilization, the same language, the same habits, the same manners and imbued with the same opinions. It proved impossible to transform this community into a federal union as Seeley wanted. Quite why is difficult to answer. Partly perhaps because of its geographical dispersion, partly the different levels of economic development, and partly too because several of its members enjoy dimensions appropriate to the present age, and by themselves are potentially very powerful. But in trading Empire for Commonwealth we have tended to delude ourselves that this group provides us with the same power-base. It does not. Politically there is no common ground. Some of its members are democratic, and some most definitely are not. Some are committed in the cold war struggle, and others are not. There is no common defence system; such formal arrangements as exist arise outside of the Commonwealth connection. The only substance left is economic under what remains of the imperial preference system. It remains important, but this too is dwindling. But if the Commonwealth gives us no real power leverage in the world it does provide us with the fantasy of space and power. And it provides us with something more, for even if the Commonwealth was disbanded tomorrow the special relationship which exists between all members of the Anglo-American world would not cease to be. And this is Britain's dilemma. In so far as we are part and parcel of this wider world we find it hard to pledge ourselves wholeheartedly to Europe, and equally, in so far as other European countries identify us with the Anglo-American world we are associated with the very forces against which they seek to unite. Yet if, by some chance, it should prove possible even now to mould this society of nations into a more purposive body, the hard geographical fact would remain, with all that it entails, that we are where we are – in Europe.

Thus in the case of Britain it has taken the best part of twenty years of crises to bring our leaders to confront the issues – the erosion and by 1957 the final elimination of our geographical security, invaluable to us throughout our history, especially in 1940; the unscrambling of the Empire and the Suez fiasco; the failure to maintain an independent deterrent and more recently some of our advanced science-based industries; but above all our chronic and continuous economic weakness that has stunted our economic growth and led to a contraction in our international operations – military, political and commercial. All these events and others have helped to bring us to an understanding and acceptance of the limitations imposed on us by our national size. Yet even now there are those among us who earnestly imagine that as things have been they remain, and envisage for Britain a great power role which we are quite incapable of sustaining. Mr Gaitskell, in the most unstatesmanlike speech of his career, could plaintively tell the delegates of the Labour Party Conference in 1962, that entry to the Common Market meant the end of a thousand years of history. Well, anybody who seriously thinks that the revolution in communications and technology does not mean the end of a thousand years of history is just not tuned in to reality. And that is about the kindest thing that can be said. Others have been less polite. Mr Acheson said that Britain had lost an empire and had not yet found a rôle, and what infuriated everybody about Mr Acheson was that he was not only rude but that he was also right.

Chapter IV

Reasons of Scale

A great deal has been said about size and it has been implied that there are substantial advantages associated with it; to such an extent, indeed, as to make large size a necessary attribute of a great power in the modern era.

A nation may be classed as 'big' or 'small' for a variety of reasons. One obvious criterion, and the one with which we have been concerned so far is geographical extension – *area*, but of no less importance, especially in military affairs, is the size of the population – *numbers*, and in considering the economic size of a country the *per capita* income – *wealth*, is of great importance also. In some measure these three criteria are interrelated. Most countries which are small in population are also small in area, and a country with a great landmass can support a large population and often has one. But clearly there is no positive correlation between these three standards of size. America, it so happens, has a large area with a large population and a high *per capita* income. China, on the other hand, has a large area with a large population but a very low *per capita* income. Japan has a large, rich population in a small area. Australia is large in area, small in numbers and rich in income, whereas Libya is large in area, small in numbers but poor in income. And Switzerland is wealthy but small in area and in population. On all three counts, Britain, when measured against the largest, is small. Her gross national product is only one-seventh that of the United States, her population would divide into China's thirteen times, and her land area into the territories of the Soviet Union one hundred times.

The things which make a nation strong or weak cannot be neatly catalogued. There are many diverse factors and it is difficult to isolate the factor of size to ascertain its impact on the power of a country. Nor is there any absolute relationship between size, in any sense, and the power and vigour of a state. There are, nevertheless, considerable advantages attached to being 'big', for defence, for economics, and, above all, for creating conditions favourable to technological progress itself.

DEFENCE

In war the advantages of size cannot be contested. Geographical space has always been an asset in defence as the enemies of Russia have repeatedly learnt to their cost, and numerical supriority, too, has usually been decisive. There are, of course, many instances where small armies have routed much larger forces, but where standards of equipment, skill, and leadership and morale are equal no army can make up for the inadequacy of numbers by the courage of their troops or the novelty and brilliance of their tactics. Ultimately, military accounts are settled by numbers.

Progress in weapons[1] technology and military transport, by increasing fire-power and the speed and range of operations, has tended to reduce the significance of numbers on the battlefield and to put an increasing premium on sheer spaciousness. According to B. Liddell Hart[1] the amount of ground that can be held by a given number of men has increased in almost direct proportion to the fire-power of defensive weapons over the last century and a half, and in offensive operations a 3 to 1 superiority is now reckoned necessary to turn the scale effectively. But if the ratio of force to space in defence has diminished, the army of industrial workers required to support the men in the field has grown, so much so that in the last war for every man at the front six were required in the factories. God still favours the big battalions.

Geographical space has gained additional importance because of the vastly increased speed and mobility of military operations. In very few countries is there now room enough for defence in depth and for strategic retreat. In the last war all the larger countries of continental Western Europe proved inadequate as military units. Only Russia and China could sustained a major military reverse and the loss of considerable land without collapsing. This was partly due to developments in aviation which by strengthening large states internally through added cohesion, and externally through the security of distance and dispersion, widened still further the power differential between large and small states.

Today the intercontinental ballistic missile has just about eliminated all plausible defensive time scales and nuclear weapons climax this development. That is why we follow a policy of deterrence in preference to defence, save in so far as conventional war may carry on beneath a nuclear stalemate. But scale also has its advantages in a deterrent strategy. The credibility of a retaliatory force rests primary on its invulnerability from surprise attack – a 'pre-emptive' strike. The invulnerability of the force can be improved in several ways – by numbers, by dispersal, by hardening and by mobility. All increase the uncertainty of a successful knock-out blow and accordingly, enhance the credibility of the deterrent. Multiplying and dispersing the targets complicates the aggressor's task, 'hardening' missiles by protecting them in underground silos increasing the problem of accuracy, and mobility creates the maximum degree of uncertainty. The larger the area of a country the greater the advantages of dispersal – mobile or static. A small country can overcome its handicap by dispersing its deterrent at sea, in space, or, if political considerations will permit, in overseas territories. A deterrent at sea enjoys the advantages of concealment, dispersal and mobility, and has the added bonus of ensuring that any attempted pre-emptive strike is not delivered on or over the land. But so long as there is no fool-proof defence against nuclear bombardment a small state can never escape its inability to absorb the destructive power of atomic weapons. The smaller the country, the few the weapons needed to destroy it, and the fewer the number needed to penetrate what defences there are. A country which is small in area, even if it can afford a deterrent system, is automatically placed at a disadvantage when threatened by one larger than itself.

A United Europe would have the industrial power, technical ability and population size to mount her own conventional defence and deterrent, if she so chose. But for reasons of scale it would be unwise to treat Western Europe as an adequate geographical unit in war. A military policy based on the assumption that her combined territories are sufficiently large to provide proper scope for dispersal and defence in depth is unrealistic. Europe cannot escape the fact that she is one of the most vulnerable areas in the world with a population density over ten times that of America and over twenty times that of Russia, with few civil defence options, contiguous urban conglomerations, and minimal warning time. Moreover, there are few areas sufficiently sparsely populated and distant from metropolitan centres to base missiles without the risk of a disarming attack doing as much damage as a counter-city strike. One leading strategist has concluded: 'Almost solely by reason of its geographical position, this crowded extension of the Asian mainland lacks the strategic options which are open to the existing great nuclear powers, with their relative inviolability to ground attack, their vast empty spaces in which to base retaliatory weapons, their distance from each other, the relative dispersion of their cities.'[2]

But perhaps it is altogether unrealistic to think in terms of advantages in relation to nuclear weapons. No geographical unit is now adequate in war. As the American scientist, Dr John von Neumann, once observed, nuclear weapons are one of those technologies for which the world is not only underorganized but also *undersized*; where we feel the effects of the finite, actual size of the globe in a critical way; where literally, and figuratively, we have run out of room.

ECONOMICS

Geographical size is also significant from an economic point of view. The greater the extent of a nation the more probable it is that it will contain a varied and an abundant base of natural resources. The larger the area the more inclusive the climate to provide a broad agricultural base, and the more multiform the geology to provide a comprehensive mineral base. Smaller nations are likely to have less variety. But it is only a probability that a large-scale country will be more richly endowed; many large countries have great tracts of desert and other waste-land useless for agriculture.

The unevenness of natural resources is a major factor in the international power equation and in some people's opinion it sets limits to the number of states who are capable of achieving great power status.[3] A small nation, it is argued, may prosper on one internationally important resource, but without a diversified resource-base it is too liable to fall under the influence of others in peace, and too vulnerable in war, ever to stand with the foremost powers.

In this respect Western Europe is highly exposed. She is rich in agriculture but poorly endowed with present-day energy resources, and wants for certain strategic minerals. But it must be remembered that a position of dependence can also be a position of strength. A country with heavy import needs may hold a unique bargaining position in international trade provided there are alternative sources of supply geographically dispersed and political unassociated. Furthermore, the resource-base of a country is not fixed and settled for all time. What is or is not a resource depends on the technology of the day. New methods of search may yield new finds. New techniques may expose resources hitherto unexploitable because they were inaccessible or unworkable. Industrial and technological advance may create a use for materials formerly regarded as worthless, or create a demand for low-grade minerals hitherto uneconomic. As high-yield resources become depleted it will become necessary to exploit lower and lower grade ores and since many countries have low-grade resources, at present uneconomic to exploit, the difference between minerally rich and poor countries will diminish. In these circumstances the resource endowment of a country will be less important than the level of its technology. The technological possibilities of expanding Europe's resource-base in the future are considerable – especially if she turns to the sea-bed for development.

The geographical size of a country also has economic significance in its bearing on the size of the market. The total demand for some equipment is a function of the area of a country. Such is the case with the demand for aircraft to be flown on domestic routes, and the same is true for a great deal of communications, transport and energy infrasturucture – coaxial cables, railway track, power transmission lines, etc. The area of a country may also have an indirect bearing on the size of the market in so far as a large country has the capacity to support a large population; the number of people, plus the scale of their purchasing power – the capacity to absorb a large annual output of goods, governs the magnitude of demand. Thus from an economic point of view a nation may be counted big or small by the size of its area, population, or *per capita* income. But again there is no precise correlation between these three. Many countries small in area have large populations, and often the level of *per capita* income is more important than either numbers or area.

Essentially, there are three sets of advantages to be derived from a large single market; those which arise from opportunities for increased specialization; those which arise from economies of scale in mass production; and those which arise from intensified competition.[4]

All countries engage in production activities unsuited to their natural endowment, capital stock and manpower. This is done to avoid over-dependence on other countries so as to safeguard against the danger of being cut-off from essential supplies. Thus for political reasons the international division of labour stops short of the economic optimum. In a large market, with mobility of capital and labour, resources can be more efficiently allocated within the area of the union – each country or region specializing in the production of those things for which it is most suited. This is the classic argument in favour of free trade. But apart from the geographical redistribution of industrial operations, an enlargement of the market also leads to changes in the structure of individual industries. Within a wider market it is possible to segregate various functions of an industry into specialized undertakings. A group of complex processes is broken down into a series of simpler processes, these then become new industries ancillary to the production of more complex final products. Such is the case with the manufacture of parts, accessories and components for motor vehicles. This allows the use of specialized machinery and specialized labour, and productivity is much increased. But large-scale operation at this stage is only economic if there is a large demand for the final product which these subsidiary industries serve. The wider the market the larger the economies of specialization. Small countries cannot always sustain the optimum operation of subsidiary and ancillary industries. The subdivision of activities is limited by the extent of their home-market.

A large market also allows the modern potentialities of production and distribution to be used to the full. With increasing plant-size, cost per unit of output tends to fall until a critical or 'optimum' size of plant is reached beyond which there are no further economies. A restricted market may fail to provide an adequate outlet for the full capacity output of the most efficient production plant. Where this is so a manufacturer must either operate equipment of the inefficient small-scale or employ the efficient large-scale plant uneconomically – that is to say on a part-time basis. When machinery and equipment can be fully exploited there are further economies for the manufacturer in planning, design, marketing and research – nonproportional activities whose costs rise less than proportionally with an increase in output.

The smaller countries of Western Europe, with populations of under 15 million, like Belgium and Holland, or with a relatively low *per capita* income, like Italy, are economically too small to enjoy all these economies of scale. The full-time utilization of a single modern plant of optimum size yields a volume of output in excess of the total domestic demand. This is the case with aircraft, oil refineries, steel rolling mills, automobiles, atomic energy production, and heavy mechanical and electrical engineering. Indeed, in some classes of industry these countries are too small to enjoy the minimum let alone the optimum scale of plant, and they are thus prevented from operating inefficiently by being prevented from operating at all.

In the larger countries of Western Europe, those with 50 million people and a fairly high *per capita* income, there are few industries for which the market is not sufficient to ensure the optimum utilization of plant. But it may be that the optimum scale of producion is greater than even these countries provide for. A country may be big enough to provide a market for at least one optimum scale plant but it will still be too small if some of these plants need equipment, servicing and intermediate products but provides too small a market for some of these. Certainly, with this size of country there are still great economies to be had from nonproportional activities, notably research, in an extended market, and there are also considerable benefits to be derived from intensified competition.

A country with dimensions great enough to ensure the *technical* optimum operation of industry may still be too small to ensure the *economic* optimum if it cannot reach optimum size without creating a monopoly or quasi-monopoly situation. Only a large market enables *several* firms to take advantage of the optimum scale of operations. In other words, it is only in an extended market that the advantages of size can be reconciled with the maintenance of competition. This is important because only competition will ensure that a country which is capable of obtaining optimum operations will *in fact* exploit the most efficient means of production, and ensure, moreover, that the resulting lowering of costs will be passed on to the consumer in lower prices. In a small home market competition is usually weak because relations are personal and cooperative.

It is often considered ungentlemanly for producers to encroach on one another's markets and in European countries in the pre-Rome Treaty days the live-and-let-live philosophy prevailed. In a large market there is less chance of collusion; competition is anonymous and more aggressive, and this spurs efficiency and progress.[5]

Increased specialization, mass production, and intensified competition all tend to increase productivity and this in turn enlarges the market by raising national incomes and augmenting demand via a reduction in the price.

However, the economic size of a nation cannot be measured solely by reference to the size of its home market. The national boundary forms a barrier to economic activities but it is not insurmountable, and the precise economic significance of the national frontier will depend on the degree of these restrictions. For some small countries international trade may be important enough to extend the national economy beyond the national border. At the same time, feeble communications and cultural diversity may be so great in a large country as to regionalize it economically into more than one market. Before 1914, when economic distance was a major impediment to trade and when artificial barriers were negligible, the difference between large and small states was of little significance economically. But unfortunately in the severely disintegrated conditions of today the overseas market does not provide a safe avenue of escape from the penalties of smallness. Specialization and mass production techniques call for large, homogeneous and stable markets *over a period of time*, and this foreign trade does not provide, subject as it is to sudden and unpredictable shifts in the level of restrictions. Management is unwilling to invest in mass-production equipment when fluctuations in market opportunities shorten production runs, and when diversified export requirements, due to the lack of cultural and technical homogeneity, hold down their productive levels. At the same time the riskiness of exports prevents effective international specialization. Any market, of course, has its hazards and the home market is certainly not immune from risks, but for several

G

reasons the riskiness of foreign transactions is much greater. Over and above the additional costs incurred in entering a foreign market there are those uncertainties associated with the complexity of foreign trade regulations. Unforeseen costs and penalties may be incurred and transactions may even be invalidated. Then there is the possibility of unilateral changes in tariffs and other restrictions to trade – quotas, surcharges, exchange measures, economic policies, not to mention devaluation, imposed for political reasons or to meet balance of payments difficulties. All these risks make it hard to obtain economic advantages of size from exports, and it is this risk factor which therefore makes the size of a nation relevant economically. A large home market is relatively secure and acts as a sort of 'springboard' for the export trade, or, to borrow an idea from geopolitics, as a sort of economic 'heartland' from which to carry out offensive operations against the rest of the world economy.

The reduction of risk is one of the strongest arguments in favour of economic integration between small countries. A customs union, unlike a free trade area, means a *permanent* commitment as far as the abolition of tariffs and other frontier restrictions are concerned. But uncertainties due to other policies remain so long as the coordination of economic policies is not achieved. This is provided for in a common market although only an economic union would guarantee completely unrestricted trade and stability.

The *Spaak Report*, the blueprint for the Common Market, argued the case for a large single market with great force and clarity: '... a fusion of the separate markets is an absolute necessity. It is that which makes it possible, by an increased division of labour, to eliminate the wastage of resources and, by a greater security in supplies, to abandon lines of production which are carried on irrespective of cost considerations ...

'This fusion of markets opens large outlets for the use of the most modern techniques. There are already productive activities which demand such vast resources, or machine tools of so great an output that they are no longer appropriate to the scale of an isolated national market. But above all, in many branches of industry, national markets offer the opportunity of attaining optimum dimensions only to firms which enjoy a *de facto* monopoly. The strength of a large market is its ability to reconcile mass production with the absence of monopoly.

'. . . in a larger market, it is no longer possible to organize the maintenance of outdated methods which result at one and the same time in high prices and in low wages; and firms, instead of preserving the *status quo* unchanged, are subjected to continual pressure to invest in order to increase production, to improve quality, and to modernize their methods: they have to progress in order to survive.'[6]

*

These then, in brief, are some of the military and economic 'reasons of scale' advanced in favour of European unification. But it is curious that among all the pleadings so little space should have been found for the technological case. In the bulk of literature on European unity no reference whatsoever is made to this argument and in the public debate on British entry in 1960–63 it never figured at all. Indeed, the Rome Treaty itself makes no reference to science and technology, and mentions the word 'research' once – in the agricultural section.

This neglect was quite consistent with the attitude of economists for whom capital accumulation was the relevant parameter in the problems of economic growth. The contribution of science and technology to growth was considered as 'exogenous' and its influence eliminated from the theoretical models. Of course economists recognized that science and technology were at the root of all human material progress but its part in the growth process was assumed rather than explicitly accounted for. Eventually, however, it began to be felt that this 'residual' factor might explain a large, if not the major part of economic growth. A series of studies in the United States confirmed this view. It was found that in mature industrial countries capital accumulation accounted for only a small part of the long-term increase in productivity, while 'technological

progress' (embracing here, education and improved organization as well as research and development) accounted for up to
90 per cent of the increase in real product per person employed.
Growth models which stressed the rise in output as being primarily dependent on the rate of capital formation and ignored
the role of technological improvements were shown to be hopelessly misleading.

Technology is the necessary condition, though not a sufficient
condition, of economic progress. What matters is not so much
the rate of capital formation as the amount of new technology
new capital incorporates. 'Investment in capital equipment may
be regarded as one immediate cause of the increase in productivity, expressed as output per man-hour. But the rise in productivity thus realized depends largely on the new technology
that is built into new capital equipment; and this new technology is the result of research, invention and development. Research and invention, in their turn, largely spring from education; and it is again education in the widest sense of the word
which creates in management and labour as well as in society
at large the psychological climate which is indispensable if innovations are not only to be made but, above all, to be put to the
most efficient economic use. Education and research may thus
be regarded as basic factors in the process of economic growth,
while investment in capital equipment may be relegated to the
role of an intermediate factor in this process.'[7]

Quite why it took economists so long to penetrate this
'fourth' factor is not completely clear. One economist has had
the candour to admit, '... that technical improvements are of
such relatively great importance should be no small cause of
concern, and possibly embarrassment, to economists who have
traditionally treated technology as exogenous in the theory of
production.'[8] Be that as it may, one consequence of this general
neglect is the relative paucity of reliable facts and figures in
this field. What statistics there are, are apt to lie more strongly
than most, and nothing of certainty is known about the 'science
of science' – the sociology of invention and the conditions,
economic, social and political, favourable to its exploitation

and progress. But during the past few years a certain amount of information has been assembled – thanks chiefly to the services of the Scientific Directorate of OECD, which has brought the technological argument into the open. It is now the talking point in Britain and Europe and is evinced as one of the strongest arguments in favour of a United Europe.

THE TECHNOLOGY GAP

Most regions of the world have made important contributions to scientific and technological progress at one time or another but for the last five centuries the pace has been set by the countries of Western Europe. It is generally agreed that so far as the advance of knowledge is concerned Europe's contribution remains impressive. Unquestionably, the Nobel Prize awards for science, if it is legitimate to use them in this way, uphold this claim. Since the Prize was created in 1901, Western Europe has taken 50 prizes for physics, 53 for chemistry and 54 for physiology and medicine, 157 science prizes in all, compared to the American total of 70 and the Russian total of 9. Taking the awards for the past six years alone, Britain, Germany and France between them have gained 17 prizes to America's 16 and Russia's 3. But the advance of knowledge is one thing, its exploitation quite another, and the plain fact is that Western Europe has now not only lost her technological supremacy but is becoming increasingly dependent on imported techniques to maintain her industrial competence.

The advanced technologies – aerospace, electronics and nuclear power, provide clear evidence of this decline. In each case the theoretical groundwork was done on this side of the Atlantic but it is America who is reaping what Europe has sown. Germany pioneered missile technology in the 1940's but in the 1960's America and Russia are the only real space powers. Several countries have succeeded in putting satellites and other instruments in orbit on the back of American technology but of the European countries only France has succeeded in doing so unaided. In the new world satellite communications system, developed and controlled (61 per cent) by the United States,

Europeans must rest content with a minority shareholding (29 per cent) even though the whole idea came from an Englishman.

Since the war the European aircraft industry, concentrated in Britain and France, has pioneered civil jet flight, rear-engine design, automatic landing systems, and VTOL flight, but of the 15 000 aircraft (9 000 for commercial and private use) and the 18 000 engines built in the world each year, 60 per cent (80 per cent in value) are built in America, 25 per cent in Russia and 15 per cent in Europe. The American aerospace industry has annual sales of 21 billion dollars while the industry in Western Europe, with almost half the aeronautical labour-force, has sales of only 2.5 billion dollars. According to *Jane's All The World's Aircraft*, in the 1965/66, France sold 24 Caravelles, and Britain 22 BAC One-Elevens, 15 Tridents and 3 Super VC-10's. The United States, by comparison, sold in the same period, 145 Boeing 707's and 720's, 180 Boeing 727's, 49 Boeing 737's, 53 Boeing 747's, 120 Douglas DC-8's and 210 DC-9's. The editor of *Jane's* adds 'It is almost superfluous to point out that the 53 Boeing 747's, by themselves, will cost a total sum of money nearly twice as great as the export earnings of the entire British aircraft industry in 1966.'

The story is repeated in the computer industry with the American giant, International Business Machines (IBM), and its compatriot General Electric, who control Olivetti's computer interests in Italy and Machines Bull in France, sharing 90 per cent of the continental market. The only viable computer industry on this side of the Atlantic which is not in American hands is in Britain. But even here home manufacturers control barely half their own market and according to present orders the value of imported installations will exceed the value of home-built installations before very long. The largest British firm is International Computers & Tabulators (ICT). They sold 178 second generation machines, as against the 10 000 of IBM, 640 of UNIVAC, 650 of RCA, 591 of Control Data Corp., 488 of Burroughs, 387 of General Electric, 226 of the National Cash Register, and 180 of Honeywell – all American concerns. Third generation computers were introduced in 1965, and by September 1966 ICT had sold 400 of their new series, but IBM had orders for 500 of their third generation machines in Britain alone, and orders for 8 000 in America.

Owing to commercial secrecy, the difficulties of sorting out new installations from replacements and the ill-defined borderline between computers and electronic calculators, accurate computer installation statistics do not exist. But the estimated computer population of a country is one of the best available indications of the penetration of modernization and automation. In 1966 it is estimated that the Common Market countries and Britain had 8 800 computers in use with a further 2 500 on order (38 per cent in industry and commerce, 17 per cent in banking and insurance, 15 per cent in universities and scientific institutions, and 17 per cent in government and state organizations). OECD have projected 18 000 as the total for all Europe by 1970. The present American figure is just about double that (34 000) and will exceed 45 000 by 1970.

Nuclear energy is the one major science-based industry where Europe has held her own, thanks to a high degree of international collaboration and the purchase of a great deal of nuclear know-how, material and equipment from America. The entire effort has involved 88 000 scientists and engineers, a capital investment of some £1 300 million, and an annual public expenditure, in the last 3 years, of almost £300 million. Britain and the Six had an installed nuclear generating capacity of 2 378 MW(e) in January 1965, and an estimated capacity of 11 273 MW(e) for 1970. Britain's total installed capacity of 3 925 MW(e) in 1967, is greater than the rest of the free-world's capacity combined. This is often considered a source of congratulation. The fact is, though, that none of this has been achieved at an economic rate, and now that nuclear energy has 'arrived' economically, it is the Americans, once more, who are moving into the lead. The nuclear export business, currently worth more than 2 billion dollars a year, is wholly dominated by two American companies, Westinghouse and General Electric, with the export of 15 power stations to their credit.

Britain, with all her expertise, has not yet sold more than 2 abroad.

Apart from this unfavourable performance in the advanced technologies, further indications of Europe's weakness are revealed in patent statistics. These must be interpreted with some caution since much valuable technical information either is not patented or is not patentable. Variations in national patent legislation and the divergent patent strategies to which these give rise also cause distortions. Nor do patent figures show the commercial and scientific value of patents. These vary enormously. However, the proportion of patents taken out by local applicants and foreign applicants in any country does give a rough indication of inventive attainment. In 1964 America issued nearly 48 000 patents in all, of which 80 per cent were issued on local inventions, the remainder being issued on inventions originating elsewhere. She also took out 56 000 foreign patents to protect her inventions abroad. In the same year Britain issued 39 400 patents of which 10 800 (27 per cent) were issued on indigenous inventions and she took out 15 000 patents abroad. Germany issued only 19 600 patents but 61 per cent of these were for German inventions and she took out 29 900 foreign patents. France has the most complete set of patent statistics. Since 1950 the total number of patents taken out by French applicants has been static around 15 000 a year, while those taken out by foreign applicants climbed from 8 000 to 25 000. During this same period France managed to increase her patent portfolio abroad by 5 000 but this did not keep pace with the penetration of foreign techniques in France. In 1960, of 51 companies who took out more than 50 patents, 21 were American, 11 were German and only 9 were French. In 1964 French holdings in the United States totalled 2 per cent of the total in that country, whereas America's holdings in France equalled 60 per cent of the domestic patents or 20 per cent of the total issued. Two-thirds of the 150 000 patents operative in France today are held by foreign applicants. The American share of total European patents is about 17 per cent, much higher than the combined Western European share of total

American patents which stands at 10 per cent, and the American share in Europe is increasing faster than the European share in America.

A more satisfactory picture of inventive attainment is provided by the flow of payments for know-how, licences and patents – 'technological balance of payments'. The royalties paid imply a process of evaluation and thus provide a crude indication of the 'productivity' of research. But again, there are difficulties of interpretation. A great deal of technological exchange is done on a barter basis, and some is given free. Payments made by subsidiaries in one country to its parent company in another are not always identifiable, and a large amount of new knowledge circulates internationally without payment, via the migratory scientist. In 1961, the United States, after paying out 63 million dollars on foreign royalties, ended up with a surplus of 514 million dollars. France, in contrast, had a deficit of 500 million francs in 1963 as against a deficit of only 93 million francs 10 years before. Germany also has a deficit – 421 million DM at the last count.[9] Britain is the only European country with a small favourable balance in technological royalty transactions – £2.9 million in 1964 with all countries.[10] However, in common with her neighbours, she had a sizeable deficit with the United States – £18 million. For Western Europe as a whole, payments to the United States exceeded receipts by 111 million dollars in 1957 and by 206 million dollars in 1961. Payments were 251 million dollars and receipts 45 million dollars – a margin of more than 5 to 1 in favour of the United States. There is no doubt that America has a large and growing favourable balance, whilst Western Europe countries have a large unfavourable balance. But again, as the OECD Report on the subject points out, a deficit may well represent an efficient and economic method of acquiring know-how and a drive towards modernization and development, and a low figure for payments could be an indication of complacency or stagnation. But what is disturbing for Europe is that her unfavourable balance is *persistent*.

Perhaps the most striking and unimpeachable evidence of

deterioration is the 'brain-drain'. The international migration
of scientists is nothing new. Before the war Europe was a 'sink'
area; her laboratories attracted hundreds of scientists from
overseas. Even today large numbers still come from the under-
developed countries of the world. What is new for Europe is a
continuing net loss of scientific manpower. OECD estimate
that between 1956/61 scientists and engineers were leaving
Europe to go to America at the rate of 2 233 a year – some
6 per cent of the annual output of science graduates. For
Britain this amounted to 7.4 per cent of the output, for
Germany 8.2 per cent, for the Netherlands 15.1 per cent and
for Switzerland 17.0 per cent. All the indications are that there
has been a much heavier loss in the past few years. The Society
of British Aerospace Companies reports that 1 300 qualified
specialists left the British industry in 1966. They either went
abroad or joined foreign subsidiaries in Britain. These included
459 draughtsmen, 613 engineers, 41 scientists and 208 technologists. Eight hundred went to America and only thirty-four
elected to go to the continent. Europe cannot afford to lose
scientific manpower on this scale when she adds only 41 400
scientists and technologists to her existing stock each year
(1963) as against the 89 000 added in America (from her own
sources) and the 142 000 added in the Soviet Union. The
United States' estimate that they gained a total of 85 000 engineers, scientists and physicians between 1949/64, and of
these 15 500 entered between 1963/64. The saving in educational costs of this influx is put at 4,000 million dollars. There
is no way of measuring the value of the output of these ent-
rants but it has been suggested that this may be greater than
the entire US foreign aid programme since 1949. Even more
alarming is the evidence that this loss is as great in terms of
quality as in quantity. Twenty-four per cent of the members
of the US National Academy of Sciences graduated abroad,
as did sixteen of America's forty-three Nobel Prize winners
for physics and chemistry.

The international movement of scientists is desirable and
can benefit all. There is no more satisfactory way of dissemin-

ating knowledge between countries. But this is true only when the exchange is reciprocated or when scientists return home with their knowledge and experience.[11] No figures exist on the extent of the emigration of American scientists to Europe, nor on how many of those European scientists who leave eventually return. But a best estimate is that of those who go, 40 per cent are gone for good.

Despite the unsatisfactory nature of much of the evidence it is clear that a serious imbalance is developing between the two sides of the Atlantic. And this gap, remember, is the consequence of the research and development efforts carried out in the late 1950's, so for all we know it may be wider still. But what of the cause? Europe's contribution to the advance of scientific knowledge remains superlative in many fields. Where Europe falls down is in translating her discoveries into commercial hardware. But why? With the present state of knowledge on the 'science of science' it would be injudicious to be too categorical, but certainly part of the explanation is to be found in the different standards of size on the two sides of the Atlantic. It was L. S. Amery, it will be recalled, who at the opening of the century suggested that in the future the people with the power of invention and science would be able to defeat all others. He did not suggest that this power might be affected by factors of size.

THE ABSOLUTE SCALE OF SCIENTIFIC EFFORT

In 1962 the United States engaged 1 159 500 scientists, engineers and other personnel on research and development (R & D) – (10.4 per thousand of the working population) and spent 17 531 million dollars – (93.7 dollars per head). In contrast, the most industrialized countries of Western Europe, Belgium, France, Holland, Germany and Britain, containing a comparable population, employed only 518 300 personnel on R & D – (4.6 per thousand of the working population) and spent 4 360 million dollars – (24.8 dollars per head). To obtain a fairer picture in making a comparison with the United States it is usual to make some allowance for the higher costs of research in America. But even with this adjustment the resources devoted to R&D are still two to three times as great in America as in Western Europe. Whether this allowance is justified is questionable because some part of these higher costs can be put down to the use of more sophisticated equipment and more highly trained personnel which *may* be purchasing more productive results. But to treat Western Europe as a single unit is definitely not a fair basis for comparison since European science is organized nationally and only to a very limited extent internationally, and there is a considerable amount of duplication – greater than can be expected within a single political state. The true extent of the gap in R & D performance can only be appreciated by measuring the total American effort against the individual national efforts of Europe. In 1962, a large country like France employed 100 000 people on R & D and spent 1 108 million dollars, and a small country like Belgium employed 21 000 people and spent 133 million dollars. When compared to the United States' effort, the ratio of financial resources devoted to R & D is of the order of 16 to 1 in the case of France, and no less than 130 to 1 in the case of Belgium.

How important is this discrepancy? The OECD Report, whose statistics have been quoted above, had this to say: 'Although the effectiveness of research and development activity is not directly proportional to the input of resources, and would in any case be subject to considerable time-lags, there is strong evidence that the much greater allocation of resources to research and development in the United States over a long period has had major economic and military effects. So far as weapons development and space research is concerned, the American (and Soviet) lead is obvious and well-known. But in the normal civilian economy, too, the greater American development effort has been an important factor in the introduction of more advanced techniques and attainment of higher levels of productivity.'[12]

The size of a country and its aggregate R & D effort has an important bearing on the rate of inventive activity for at least four good reasons. First, a large and more diversified economy can make better use of the results of basic research and of the inventions made in individual industries. If the industry in a country is specialized the chance of exploiting discoveries made in other industries is lost. Second, the research expenditure in some fields is so costly in cash and talent that a small country, *ipso facto*, is excluded from going it alone. The development of atomic energy, space research and oceanography provide examples. However, advanced technological projects of this kind not only require huge financial and technical resources, they also compel the integration of a large number of scientific and industrial activities. The more advanced the technology the larger and more complex the industrial and scientific base needed to support it. For this reason also, a small nation with a narrow range of industrial and scientific activities is excluded from these projects. But, as we shall see, it is precisely because these 'lead' technologies associate a large number of techniques that they exert a profound influence on the overall rate of technological progress. Third, a small country will not be able to cover many important fields of research, yet due to the interdependence of technologies the wider and more diversified the research activities the greater the possibilities of success. In the long run the interaction of one technique on another is likely to generate conditions more favourable to progress, and the rhythm of advance will be superior in those countries who can afford to undertake research covering all the essential sectors of scientific activity. Finally, there is the straightforward statistical probability that the more people you have working away the more bright ideas and discoveries they will unearth over a period of time.

Professor C. D. Edwards has summed up the technological advantages of large states: 'Technological and institutional change are more probable in large countries ... because there are more resources to invest in change. The large country has more funds for research, a field for experiment wide enough to try a greater number of new proposals, and more trained people who may develop new ideas. The statistical probability of a flash of genius is presumably no greater per thousand of population in a big country than in a small one; but there are not only more people to have flashes, there are also the technicians to carry out a systematic programme of research large enough to explore all the variant possibilities implicit in a particular bright idea. Forms of business organization and market organization, as well as technology in the narrow sense, are likely to be more dynamic for these reasons. Moreover, in the technological field the fact that the limits of any single patent run with the national boundaries means that the best market for a patent is likely to lie in a large country and that the expenses of development are most likely to be quickly recovered in a large economy. The flow of technological ideas across national boundaries is likely to be more conspicuous from the small countries to the large than in the reverse direction.

'Thus the dynamic forces of variety and change . . . tend to be stronger in big countries than in small ones.'[13]

Now statistics reveal no correlation between national R & D expenditures and the rate of economic growth in the medium term. Britain, for example, has spent a higher proportion of her GNP on R & D during the past decade than any of her European neighbours. In 1962 she spent 2.2 per cent compared with the average 1.4 per cent of EEC members. But her rate of growth is far slower than any of these countries – 2.6 per cent per year compared with 4.4 per cent in France and 4.7 per cent in Germany between 1955 and 1964. In the same period Japan's productivity grew 3.5 times faster than Britain's, but she spent only a little over half as much on R & D. Is it possible to deduce from this, as some people have, that the aggregate R & D effort is not as important as is made out? Certainly not, because from the point of view of economic growth what matters is not only the total R & D activity but how and for what purpose it is spent. To begin with, some resources are devoted to basic or fundamental research, (high energy physics or radio astronomy) which is performed solely to advance the frontiers of science and where no immediate economic results are in prospect. Then again, research in some areas has greater growth potential than in others – as in *production* technology as distinct from *product* technology. In addition, a large part of the R & D effort is not directed to economic ends but is just as valuable for all that; the advance of knowledge is not only desirable for its contribution to economic growth. There is research in defence, medicine, road safety, fire, air and water pollution, noise etc. These may have an indirect bearing on growth but their effect is not measurable. It must also be borne in mind that R & D is concerned with extending and improving knowledge whereas economic growth depends more on the success of applying existing science and technology. In the medium term it is related to the existing stock of knowledge rather than the flow of new knowledge. Indeed, it is quite possible for a country to have too many QSE's (qualified scientists and engineers) creating new knowledge and too few engaged in exploiting it at the production, management and sales end of the innovative process.[14] The lack of any correlation between national R & D expenditures and economic growth in the medium term signifies little and certainly does not invalidate the importance of the aggregate level of R & D activity.

Andrew Shonfield is another authority who argues that the total sum devoted to industrial research in Europe is inadequate by the standards of the technological pace set in America and Russia, and that in the long run it is the absolute level of expenditure that matters. 'We must be quite clear about the fields of research in which we can afford to do less than the Americans. About the most phoney argument on this whole subject is the one that starts out from a comparison of *per capita* expenditure on research in Britain and the United States, as if research were some kind of commodity like food or drink whose proper level of output depended on the number of individual appetites for it. The truth is, of course, that unless a national industry is pooling its research effort with the industries of other nations ... it will probably lose out in the competition for the development of new products, when it fails to match the research effort of its competitors in quantity or quality. It is altogether too facile to assume that the quality of the British research effort is likely to be so much better that it will offset the huge discrepancy in the sheer weight of money spent in foreign countries, particularly in the United States. This is the kind of thing that scientists are inclined to suggest, when one faces them with international comparisons of the size of their research effort; but it is best treated as an example of a certain vocational arrogance. . . .'[15]

B. K. Blunt believes that the advantages of 'bigness' are even greater. Like L. S. Amery he also sees science and technology as the main factor enabling a nation to prosper in peace and to conquer in war – the master variable in the geopolitical equation: 'Science enables a country consciously to examine its national resources and plan, if it so wishes, to occupy the position in the world which these resources, properly exploited, would allow.' But in the final analysis a nation's capacity to maximize its power and influence through science depends on three sets of variables – the relative number of its first class scientific minds (genius), the relative number of technicians it has to support and apply their work, and the level of awareness of the country's leaders of the potentialities of science. The difference between countries with respect to the level of awareness is diminishing. Leaders are becoming increasingly alive to science as a factor deciding the fate of nations, and in an age when all governments strive to maximize their scientific resources, the differences between nations therefore will come to depend more and more on the other two variables. To both, the size of a country's population sets absolute limits. Genius is a random phenomenon and thus when opportunities are equal, where for the moment they are not, the number of genius turning up in a country will be directly proportional to the size of its population – 'In the incidence of potential genius there is no master race'. And so God it appears is still on the side of the big battalions. '. . . in the future power will move away from the relatively small, now highly advanced nations, and the great centres of population in Asia will come into their own. China and India will become leading nations, eclipsing, perhaps, even Russia and the United States, and the little countries of Europe – Britain and Germany, France and

Holland, will sink into obscurity. This is not a pleasing prospect, and there is only one ray of comfort. A really United Europe would not be negligible, only just a first-class power perhaps, but it would have a future.'[16]

This theory, as it stands, is unacceptable. Putting aside the question of whether or not creative genius appears by chance (and the possibilities of manipulating the human brain or copying it electronically) it unjustifiably underplays the importance of factors other than size in determining the rate of inventive activity, and assumes that simply because governments are alive to the value of science they will succeed in eliminating the psychological and institutional barriers to change, and will be able to bring into existence the optimum climate for creative effort and the exploitation of human talent. This is seriously open to doubt.[17] The theory also neglects the possibility of small countries acquiring the results of research done by others. Just as contemporary innovations may draw on the basic or applied research of an earlier generation, so it may draw on the research work of another country. There is no innate reason why the successive steps of a technological innovation – research, development, testing, innovation and production, should all take place in a consistent time sequence, nor any reason why all these events should take place within one and the same country.[18] At one time, though not so much today, Japan did little original R & D but applied foreign developed processes and techniques very successfully. And America herself leant heavily on European research before the last war and even today purchases 63 million dollars worth of foreign know-how each year. Furthermore, specialization in science can help to offset the greater resources of a larger country – something else this theory ignores.

There are, nevertheless, serious objections to specialization and to over-reliance on 'vicarious research'. Some of the problems of specialization have already been intimated. Science is not easily divisible and progress often proceeds from interaction between several branches. Developments in one area may affect progress in an apparently unrelated field. The problem

H

for a country which specializes too narrowly is that it loses the bearing of one branch of science upon another. This not only exercises a delaying effect on technological progress in general but may also jeopardize the chance of staying ahead in the selected field since it is often indispensable to combine several discoveries, relevant to totally different domains, to ensure technical advance in a defined sector.

As to vicarious research, there are the usual political and strategic arguments against over-dependence. But too much second-hand research may also lead to cultural impoverishment. The skill of scientific and industrial manpower may decline through lack of experience in new specializations and novel techniques, with the danger that still more capable QSE's would drift abroad to countries where more interesting and stimulating work is to be found. The EURATOM Commission has warned '. . . to confine itself to importing what others have invented, to applying discoveries in which it has had no part, would indeed be hazardous. The danger for Europe would be that before very long it would have nothing but second class industries, techniques and manpower.'[19]

There are other hazards. In the past, it is true, technical information, with the exception of military secrets, has been one of the most mobile factors in international transactions. For the results of pure research, which are of little immediate economic significance, this is still so, but in the case of applied research the iron curtains have been rung down. R & D is very big business and owing to the delays, cost and other difficulties of protecting know-how, nationally and internationally, a substantial and increasing proportion of technical information is now never disclosed – hence the increasing profitability of industrial espionage. (This incidentally, is another way in which technological transfers are effected between countries, and at a comparatively low cost. Many technical secrets relating to defence and industry have been 'passed' through intelligence services. Several foreign embassies in London and Washington are very active in this field.) In any event, the fees from licences, patents, and know-how are never as profitable as those to be had from the export of the products of the prospective licensor during the initial phase when the new article holds a *de facto* monopoly of the market. Direct exports are always preferable when feasible. Even when the results of research are for sale it is usual to stipulate that the licensee should not compete in the home market or export market of the licensor. The operation of the license is then confined to the home market of the buyer and this means a major restriction on exports. Copying other people's research, moreover, does not result in a technical lead but a lag of several years, and owing to the complexity and cost of information retrieval across national frontiers this time-lag is aggravated in international transfers. In an industry where technical progress is very rapid this creates a considerable handicap. And finally, it must be remembered, that even when imported technology is preferred it is still necessary to maintain a strong R & D capacity in order that the information obtained can be adapted to local market and manufacturing conditions, improved and refined. Licensing arrangements are only supplementary to one's own development work. The stronger a country's own R & D and patents position, the better the chance of obtaining, through cross licensing and patent pools, technological information from another country on favourable terms. Imported know-how is rarely a complete substitute for indigenous research.

A useful way in which transnational transfers of technology occur is through the agency of foreign subsidiaries. The host country derives advantages from the results of research performed in the parent country without itself investing in the research work. There is little doubt that European industry has derived considerable benefits from American-owned subsidiaries by this means. One study suggests that in 1955 American industry made available 25–30 per cent of its own research results to American affiliations in Britain. This corresponded to an expenditure of between 400–500 million dollars.[20] But the extent to which these transfers benefit the host country's economy depends upon the propensity of American subsidiaries to export, and the degree to which this is offset by their imports of components, parts, and accessories. This is often on such a scale that the overall balance is negative. Also to be taken into account is the flow of royalty payments since it seems that in at least 60 per cent of the cases overseas subsidiaries must make payment for the know-how they acquire from parent companies. In Britain, in 1964, more than half of the total payments to overseas concerns was made by foreign-owned subsidiaries to their overseas parent companies – two-thirds (£16 million) to American parent companies.[21]

However, when research is imported on a large-scale in the form of finished results this does not diminish the research gap in terms of research performance and may even lead to a lowering of research standards and intensity. Technology transfers through the intermediary of a foreign firm's affiliations only benefit the host country's science and technology when research is performed *within* the host country itself, either in the firm's own laboratories employing local scientists and engineers, or in the local universities and research institutions. In 1964 American subsidiaries spent 400 million dollars on research executed abroad, and in addition the United States' government spent 100 million dollars in overseas universities or research establishments. IBM has a vast programme of research organized on an international basis. Fundamental and applied research is executed in Switzerland, Britain, France, Germany, Holland, Sweden, Austria and Japan. Each laboratory does specialized work and the whole programme is carefully co-ordinated with IBM's main research centres in America. Unfortunately IBM is something of an exception. According to the findings of a survey by the Stanford Research Institute,[22] subsidiaries of American firms in Europe have a lower research intensity in Europe than in America – the ratio of R & D staff to total staff is lower and so is the ratio of expenditure to sales. In most cases it is much lower – on average only 4 per cent of total R & D budgets being spent in Europe. In some cases there is no European-based research at all.[23] Even when R & D has been established, it tends to be subordinate to research centred in America. It is difficult to avoid the conclusion that many American firms regard their European research as a means 'for the more effective monitoring of European research and development, and of gaining an entry to the European scientific community'. In fact, foreign affiliations function to a large extent as 'talent scouts' for their parent companies and also for their home country's research institutes.

Parasitism, in short, is no answer for the problems of small countries, although equally, at the other extreme, national autarchy is not a viable policy, even for the very largest. That specialization and imported know-how can help to offset some of the advantages of larger countries is indisputable, but when faced with all the difficulties of specialization and the dangers of too much vicarious research, the natural tendency of small countries is to spread their intellectual and financial resources thinly over a broad scientific front, with the result, often, that their effort remains below the threshold set by others with whom they are in international competition. And in this way the real disadvantages of being small are compounded.

THE STIMULUS OF ADVANCED TECHNOLOGIES

On both sides of the Atlantic a large fraction of total R & D resources is committed to the military/space sector. In America this proportion of the total effort is higher than in Europe – in 1962, 52 per cent as against 20 per cent for Western Europe as a whole (39 per cent in Britain, 30 per cent in France, 15 per cent in Germany) or, 9 000 million dollars as against the 1 200 million spent collectively by Europe's Big Three. The US/Europe ratio in the military/space sector is therefore greater than in the civil sector, about 7 to 1. Some people, who regard this commitment as a diversion of cash and brainpower away from growth-oriented research, see this as an advantage for Europe. Let America squander her resources on these security and prestige projects which deter the advance of industrial techniques and reduce the rate of growth; Europe can concentrate her effort on stimulating the civil sector, and raise the value of real *per capita* output.[24]

Now this view begs several questions. First of all it is by no means clear that this is a diversion of resources. No one has shown that expenditures for pure research, or for research aimed directly at industrial application, are less because of the military and space programme than they would otherwise be. Moreover, even if the military/space R & D were reducing nonspace R & D, no one has shown that it is politically possible to get expenditures for R & D allocated on a more rational basis. In the past it has proved next to impossible to obtain large monies for industries where there are no strategic or prestige considerations at stake, and where the technical possibilities and sales prospects are uncertain, or even unascertainable. Perhaps this will prove possible in an age when all governments strive to maximize their resources and seek to establish proper national priorities for science, but the fact remains that at present Britain, for example, is prepared to lavish hundreds of millions of pounds on aircraft projects, but only a million and a half pounds over a three year period on a major technology like desalination. In addition, it is also true that nuclear energy, air transport, telecommunications, computers, radar and other innovations have been developed earlier and more rapidly as a result of military/space funding where cost and other commercial criteria are not the first consideration.

Over and above all this there are many people who claim that the concepts, knowledge, techniques, products and processes developed in the military/space sector are recuperable by non-military industries, and that indeed these advanced projects exert a powerful influence on the overall rate of technological progress in a nation.

Opinion on this point is sharply divided. Nobody denies that there is 'spin-off' (sometimes called fall-out or spillover) from advanced projects working at the frontiers of science, but sceptics affirm that these claims have been wildly exaggerated, and that in any case there are great difficulties in adopting military technologies or space devices for civil use, in part because of the growing divergence between military and civilian technology, in part because of security requirements which restrict the free flow of information, and in part because military/

space R & D is relevant to certain industrial sectors only. These advanced projects, say the sceptics, cannot be supported purely for their incidental benefits. If they cannot be justified on their own merits then the huge sums of money and talent they ensnare are best allocated to areas more directly relevant to the civilian economy. 'The obvious conclusion one must reach ... is that the technological fall-out from the space programme is spread extremely thinly on the ground; that the benefits that accrue bear scant relation to the colossal funds and effort invested. In other words, investment in a space programme is neither an economic nor a noticeably speedy way of advancing a nation technologically. There is little doubt that far more spectacular benefits could be derived from spending comparable sums in fields of applied research more directly aimed at improving the lot of man on Earth.'[25] This of course still begs the question over funding, but anyway who is right?

From time to time enraptured accounts have appeared of the manifold and wondrous benefits spawned from the space race.[26] These can be discounted. The most sober, objective assessment of the matter is a report by the Denver Research Institute.[27] Six ways were identified in which missile/space R & D had contributed to the commercial economy. They were: the stimulation of basic and applied research; the development of new processes and techniques; the development of new products; the improvement of existing products; increased availability of materials and equipment; cost reductions through the improvement of production techniques, and a fuller utilization of research facilities. This 'spin-off' was classified in three categories – tangential, tangible and intangible. *Tangential* benefits arose in two ways. Intensive use of certain technologies by the missile/space industries had made equipment and materials relating to this field more readily available for commercial use. Equipment which formerly had to be made to special order could now be bought off the shelf. Second, the volume of production for missile/space use reduced the unit cost of an item to the point that large scale commercial marketing became feasible. *Tangible* spin-off was defined as the transfer to commercial use of identifiable products, processes or materials, originally developed for space applications. *Intangible* spin-off, on the other hand, was defined as the transfer of scientific and technological *information* – new knowledge – to commercial use. The Report confirmed the view of the sceptics that technology designed to meet the specific needs of space was usually quite different from that required by the civilian industry, with the result that although there had been some tangible 'spin-off' from space research it had been small and insignificant to date. Owing to a time-lag of some five to ten years however, between development and exploitation, an accurate assessment could not be made. Nor did this imply that there was not an appreciable quantity of potential 'spillover' which had not yet been retrieved by the civilian economy. Furthermore, the Report claimed that *intangible* 'spin-off', although it had received scant recognition, was far more important than the tangible benefits, and that basic research in almost all the sciences conducted for the purposes of space exploration had yielded new information valuable to electronics, metals, fuels, the life sciences, ceramics, instrumentation, thermals and cryogenics. The difficulty was to identify it, for by the time space developed information was put to commercial use it had usually been combined with information from many other sources. The Report stated in conclusion: 'The total contribution of missile/space R & D to the commercial economy is broader, more complex, more indirect, and more difficult to identify than is generally realized. . . . Because of the scope and complexity of the total contribution, it is probably more significant than is frequently envisioned, although this significance does not appear to lend itself to quantitative measurement.'

These findings corroborate the 'forcing-function' thesis, according to which there are certain 'lead' technologies that force the pace of development in others, setting a tempo of advance superior to what could otherwise be attained. A 'lead' technology has been defined by the Cranfield Society: 'The interdependence of modern industries is such that one can assign leading roles to some industries and slave roles to others.

How one defines these industries largely depends on the terms of reference. An industry can be said to lead if it has a higher productivity and a better export record than any others. Such an assessment is from economic considerations, and quite justifiable, but it is not the only test of leadership. . . . The other basis for judgement is in the capacity of an industry to stimulate developments in others. This is surely the most valid test of leadership, since it is the capacity to develop and assimilate new ideas which ultimately determines the progress of a country's industry. New ideas are not spontaneously generated throughout industry, they require stimuli, and it is the industry which provides these stimuli, or fall-out, which is the true leader industry.'[28] What is not so clear is how this stimulus is imparted or why it should be necessary. But the answer, it seems, is that complex projects of an applied nature like space research, working ahead of existing knowledge, compel the integration of a large number of scientific and industrial activities and so provide a meeting ground for many diverse technologies and an environment favourable for interaction, cross-fertilization and mutual stimulation. At the same time, by setting a firm objective, they integrate the efforts of scienists and engineers in a way that cannot be achieved by a disconnected series of research investigations – a further stimulus to creativity. In this regard, space research is considered unequalled, in part because of the great technical difficulties posed by space conditions, and in part because of the wide span of industries embraced by a space programme.

But pace-setting is not the sole prerogative of space research. The nuclear energy industry has performed a similar service: '. . . the use of nuclear power draws on a very wide range of industries, which, to comply with nuclear technical requirements, need to improve the quality of their output and engage in research for that purpose. The atom is unquestionably an element in that technical progress which is the mainspring of economic prosperity.'[29] In this case the stimulus appears to be more direct. It is not so much that it leads to any specific nuclear technology as to the adoption by classical industry of new techniques and methods to cope with the stringent requirements of nuclear industry.

The aircraft industry has also been a stimulus to technological progress. The Plowden Committee's Report on the British aircraft industry identified 'spin-off' from aviation projects covering, specifically, digital computers, hydraulic systems, gas turbines, electronics, radar and radio, and more generally, materials, production methods, structures, aerodynamics, mechanical engineering, propulsion and power plants: 'The evidence convinces us that the technological fall-out from the aircraft industry is important ... it seems probable that no other single industry would have such a pervasive effect on the technological progress of the nation. The industry has a unique combination of characteristics ... together these characteristics have led to engineering standards higher than in most other industries ... only the aircraft industry embraces so wide a range of scientific and engineering skills. It covers aerodynamics, materials, structures, hydraulics, instrumentation, propulsion, fuels, electrics and electronics. It is through these skills that the high standards of the aircraft industry are spread, both to directly linked industries such as electronics, computers and telecommunications, and beyond.'[30]

That any complex project which genuinely advances the frontiers of knowledge acquires information with potential application elsewhere is not in doubt. What is debatable is the precise importance of this intellectual and material feedback and whether or not a comparable rate of technical progress can be generated in the absence of the stimulus provided by a major enterprise of great technical difficulty. The full impact of the space race on technological progress, owing to the time-lag before commercial application, will not be felt until the next decade, but if it is as important as the Denver Institute's Report suggests, and if the same rate of progress cannot be made without the stimulus of a 'lead' technology, then 'spin-off' can be advanced as a major justification for these projects – although, in point of fact, they can stand on their own merits in many cases.

On this point the Plowden Committee were equivocal. After considering whether greater scientific and technical progress might be achieved if the large number of scientists and engineers in the industry worked more directly on the problems involved, they came to the conclusion that '... taking a long view, the technological fall-out from the industry cannot be advanced as a major justification for support to ensure that the industry survives or is maintained at any particular level... the strength of the fall-out argument in the long-term depends on what general Government policy is adopted for technology. The more money and effort the Government is prepared to put into systematically encouraging the *use* of advanced technology throughout British industry, the less it need rely on the stimulus of the aircraft industry.' Now this conclusion may very well be right for the aircraft industry, but the Plowden Committee have in fact side-stepped the main point at issue. The stimulus of advanced technology, according to the findings of the Denver Research Institute, is primarily in the creation of *new knowledge*, not its application. Although 'lead' technologies do act as a stimulus to innovation and renovation in industry, their 'unique' impulse is in the rate of acquisition of new information, for reasons which the Report itself had outlined earlier: '... against the apparent wastefulness of deriving technological progress as a by-product must be set the difficulty of fixing the objective when tackling problems directly. In building aircraft, demands are pitched higher than the person who receives the eventual fall-out, or any government research committee concerned with predicting his needs, would set them. The stimulus of having to meet a deadline for the rest of a project produces a concentration of effort and a speed of advance not otherwise attainable.' The clue to this apparent inconsistency is to be found in paragraph 170 of the Committee's Report: 'More broadly, we believe that the wider spread of technological progress in industry is limited not so much by the volume or nature of the new discoveries or advances being made by the nation's scientists and engineers, or even the areas in which they are being made, as by industry being unaware of them and unwilling to apply them.' Perhaps, but ultimately it is the speed at which new discoveries, new information and new inventions become available that will determine the rate of all innovative activity and the competitiveness of nations. There will be no profit in being second. The question that has to be answered in this: are 'lead' technologies or industries unique in the speed at which they force forward the frontiers of science, or can a comparable rate of progress be accomplished by more direct means? The answer is crucial to determining scientific priorities.

The truth of the matter is that we simply do not know, and until very much more is known about the 'science of science' the issue will remain unresolved. Only one thing remains beyond dispute. During the past two decades when America and Russia have put such a colossal effort into the missile/space sector, and when the countries of Western Europe, individually have found it difficult or impossible to participate effectively in these ventures, and at the same time have not made much effort in direct growth-oriented research, the small countries have been at a disadvantage compared with those large enough to do so. This has been another factor of size contributing to Western Europe's technological weakness.

LARGE FIRMS AND THE SIZE OF THE MARKET

On the whole, American companies are very much larger than their European competitors in corresponding industries. According to the directory of the world's largest companies published each year by the business magazine *Fortune*, America has 306 and Europe 140 (Britain 54 and EEC members 74) of the top five hundred. Such giant European concerns as Volkswagenwerk (Germany), Philips' Gloeilampenfabbrieken (Holland), Fiat (Italy), Renault (France), ARBED (Luxembourg) and Petrofina (Belgium), which are in fact the largest in their own countries, rank 5th, 7th, 12th, 18th, 45th, and 70th, respectively, on the European list of largest companies, but only 24th, 27th, 43rd, 73rd, 129th and 140th, respectively, on the world list. The *Union des Industries de la*

Communauté Européenne (UNICE), which represents the interests of industry in the Six, has made an analysis of the size of companies in the western world on the basis of *Fortune's* figures.[31] Apparently, the annual sales of the twenty largest American companies are equal to the entire Gross National Product of Germany, while those of the five largest alone equal that of Italy. General Motors, the world's largest company, has sales which exceed the German Federal Budget and are equal to the combined sales of Germany's thirteen largest companies. Another contrast that is drawn is the ratio of the size of the largest Coummunity firm (as measured by turnover) to its opposite number in the United States. In chemicals the turnover of the largest Coommunity firm is 42 per cent that of the largest American company; in rubber it is 35 per cent; in automobiles 10 per cent; in steel 44 per cent; in petroleum 63 per cent; and in electricals 35 per cent. Amongst other evidence of the American predominance is the fact that of the world's companies with sales of over 250 million dollars a year each, America has 82 per cent of those in mechanical engineering and 60 per cent of those in electrical engineering, and perhaps it is significant that these are just the sectors where Europe's balance of patents-payments are most adverse.

These facts and figures cause concern in Europe and especially in France where there are comparatively few firms of international size, and where 90 per cent of all companies employ less than ten people. But as the UNICE Report was careful to point out, it is easy to exaggerate their importance: 'Expansion in size alone is neither a universal nor a uniform requirement in an enlarged market: it is more or less desirable – and can even be undesirable – according to the technology of the industry in question, the incidence of transport costs on final product cost, the discrimination in customers' requirements and the degree of specialization ... it is important therefore that on the basis of the present study no generalizations should be made which it was not the intention of the authors to draw.'

Some of the advantages of bigness in regard to large-scale production and distribution have already been considered, but it is in R & D that the main benefits occur. They arise through the element of *cost*, the element of *time*, and the element of *risk*, in research.

R & D is an expensive occupation and only large corporations have the resources to finance the laboratories and expensive equipment necessary to the discovery of new knowledge and its application. To take one example: the average research expenditure needed to produce a new medicine based on a single chemical entity is now estimated as £2 million, and it costs at least £300 000 to bring a potentially promising range of compounds to the point where it becomes clear that the promise will not be fulfilled, and that that particular line of research can be abandoned. There is thus an initial level of R & D expenditure below which a research programme is just not feasible. It varies from industry to industry, but in many cases the fixed cost is greater than can be borne by the small enterprise. That is why R & D is concentrated in a few large firms, and why the percentage of firms undertaking R & D increases steadily with the size of firm. In the United States 89 per cent of all firms employing more than 5 000 people undertake research and between them they account for 85 per cent of the total industrial research effort. Firms employing between 1 000 and 5 000 people account for only 8 per cent of industrial research expenditure. Similarly in Britain, 90 per cent of the firms employing more than 2 000 people carry on R & D and between them perform 93 per cent of the research in industry. Those employing less than 300 people account for only 1 per cent.[32]

Another advantage for the big firm is that they have longer economic time-horizons necessary for long-term development plans. In the past the gestation period from the conception of an idea to the first working model (research), and from the model to economic production (development), was not infrequently as long as eighty years – the case with the fluorescent lamp. The zip fastener took twelve years of research and eighteen of development; the tape recorder five of research and thirty-five of development; the self winding watch one year's research and sixteen for development. R & D times have steadily decreased since the war and in some cases they are very short indeed – the transistor took only five years, but even now the time-lag between a really fundamental discovery in science and widespread application is rarely less than twenty years. Only large firms can afford to wait that long for the pay-off. Marconi did not pay a dividend during its first thirteen years of operation, and more recently RCA had to wait nearly fifteen years for a profit from the 130 million dollars it spent on launching colour television. Today many large American corporations do their technological planning for twenty and even thirty years ahead. Few European firms can afford that length of time for a return on their money.

The risk and uncertainty in R & D is far greater than in any other type of investment. 'Science is original, and therefore unpredictable' and only large firms can afford to underwrite the risks of failure. They also have the resources to pursue several lines of research at the same time. In a multiple strategy successes have some chance of being in statistical balance with failures, and many failures have to be faced and must be financed by one eventual success. A large firm is also typically a diversified firm; bigness is achieved through a spread across a wide span of products and industries rather than by dominance of a single industry. The greater the diversification the more likely it is that the results of research will be used. Unanticipated findings are more readily recognized and therefore utilized; research results are more likely to be in line with the company's existing activities, and new knowledge acquired can be used over a wider field. The degree of uncertainty is correspondingly reduced. It is for this reason also that the large, diversified firm is more disposed to do basic research – being a more open-ended process it has bigger risks and a longer time perspective than applied research or development work. In America only 16 per cent of medium-sized firms undertake basic research whereas 47 per cent of the large firms do so. However, despite the great risks and uncertainties involved, it is in basic research that the really significant breakthroughs are made,

and thus, generally, it is the many-product giant that is technologically most dynamic.

Diversification tends to increase with the size of firm and so
here, too, America's larger-sized firms give her the advantage.
A study of the thousand largest manufacturing companies in
the United States revealed that among the largest fifty concerns,
twenty-six operated in more than fifteen industries, and thirty-
three made shipments in more than twenty product classes.
Only seventy-eight of the thousand confined their production to
one class of product.

Yet another chance for the big firm to reduce the risks and
uncertainties inherent in research is provided by their control
over the market. They are better placed to recover R & D expenditure. The cost of basic research is a fixed cost, independent of output, and the cost of applied research and development rises less than proportionately with the increase in output.
Returns rise as output increases.

Economists have never been able to agree among themselves
as to the precise importance of big business in promoting technological progress. One faction, led by Schumpeter and
Galbraith,[34] regard the giant corporation as the prime-mover of
progress. The cost and risks of innovation are so great that
only the large firm can afford to become involved. They alone
have sufficient control over the market necessary if the returns
from innovations are to be recouped. The expense is just too
much and the prospective returns too uncertain, too distant and
too insufficiently recoverable for the small company to contem-
plate an active R & D programme. So the argument runs.

On the other hand, there are those who say that this is not
so, and that 'atomistic competition' is still the best form of
industrial set-up to foster rapid technological change. It is only
the fear of being overtaken, displaced or disinherited that in-
duces firms to innovate. There is nothing like a strong dose of
competition to stimulate progress. In such circumstances research is necessary to survive. Evidence is then produced to
show that the largest firms do not in fact make the most intensive research efforts; that in proportion to their sales, medium-

sized firms (of those who do research) spend more than large companies.[35] This seems to neglect the economies of scale at the higher level, but in any case from our point of view, considering reasons for the technology gap, it is irrelevant whether firms are inclined to do more or less research *relative to their size*. What concerns us is not the *proportionate* expenditure but the greater *absolute* level of expenditure of large firms. A country with a few large concerns is still likely to do more industrial research than a country with many smaller firms simply because so few small firms do any research, while almost all large firms do so. It might be recalled that the German firm, I. G. Farben, established its commanding lead in the plastics industry between the wars simply by spending more money on plastics research (7–10 per cent of their turnover) than any other chemicals firm.

The query is then raised as to whether the fertility of research is correlated with size. Patents statistics are produced which show that the inventive output per dollar spent is lower in large firms than in some medium-sized firms.[36] The limitations of patent data have already been stressed. It is not only the number of discoveries and inventions that is significant, but their economic and scientific value. Furthermore, a great deal of technological information is not disclosed (or is not patentable) and there is evidence to suggest that the larger the firm the more secretive it is. This follows from the fact that basic research, which large firms are more disposed to do, yields discoveries and information which is not patentable, and in order to profit from this expensively acquired information it is necessary to keep it secret from competitors. But again, from our point of view, all this is of little consequence, for what matters is not the relative fertility count but the *absolute* level of inventive output. I. G. Farben, by spending more money than anyone else in the interwar years, took out twice as many patents as its nearest rival, and accounted for a third of all patents taken out by the thirty leading chemical firms and for 17 per cent of all plastics patents in those years.

Another line of attack against size is the argument that the

I

days of the lone inventor are not yet over; that the research laboratories of the large industrial corporation have not been responsible for the greater part of significant inventions in the past fifty years; that they still rely heavily upon other sources of original thinking; and that in any event in some cases the giant laboratory may positively stifle creative activity.[37] Perhaps this is so for the past. It may or may not be true for the future. It does not appear to be the case where inventions require a systematic search for new knowledge with expensive equipment, nor does the argument stand examination in the infinitely more costly and lengthy business of development – bringing an idea, invention or discovery, to the production stage. Again the plastics industry is instructive. Out of the total 6 238 patents issued between 1946–55, 92 per cent were taken out by corporations and only 8 per cent by individuals, and nylon cost 20 million dollars to develop.[38]

These criticisms of bigness underscore the point that the case for greater size in industrial organization can be pressed too far. They do not destroy the case, but show that new ideas and discoveries arise from a great variety of sources and that the big corporation is not the sole instrument of progress. However, there is another problem of research, relating to the element of time, ignored by these arguments, which confers major competitive advantages on the big firm. This is the problem of 'lead time' – a concept borrowed from defence thinking on the missile gap and armaments race.

Lead time is the time taken from the first designation of a new product to its production in quantity. That is to say, the time it takes to carry an original idea right through the various stages of innovation – research, development, prototype or pilot-plant, testing, scaling up to first full-scale size, de-bugging, commercial production and sales. In a science-based industry, which lives off research, competition is not only through the price of existing products but also by the speed with which new or technically better products can be brought onto the market. Since speed is of the essence technical change tends to be very rapid and product-life short. In electronics, product life lasts between three and ten years – five for computers, seven for marine radar, and only one to three years for certain types of equipment. The life cycle of home appliances is now put at eight years whereas it was thirty-four years for products introduced before 1920. In these circumstances a short lead time can be a major competitive advantage – rendering all rival products obsolete. And equally, too long a lead time may be fatal.

Typical lead times vary from industry to industry and product to product. For an advanced computer system it is put at five to six years, for a communications satellite five years, for a TV colour camera four years, for a spectrum analyser three years, and for radio communications receivers two years.[39] For improvements and minor advances it may be only a matter of months.

Now lead times can be reduced in various ways. Efficient planning and the use of control techniques are essential for a start. Luck, skill, ingenuity, inspiration and perspiration are a great help. But lead times can also be drastically cut by simply putting more men on the job. The speed of advance bears some relationship to manpower committed. There are several reasons for this. First, in any research project there is always a certain amount of routine hack work that has to be got through, and the more people on the job the sooner this is likely to be cleared. There are also always a number of potential lines of approach to the solution of a problem, and the greater the number it is possible to follow up the better the chance of reaching a satisfactory result. Sometimes, indeed, a multiple strategy is indispensable since it is the combined results of a number of lines of inquiry that yield the answer.

There is another aspect of the multiple approach. At the start of a development programme estimates of the cost, development time and product performance of the various alternative routes are subject to great uncertainty. It is impossible to know which is the best avenue. A firm with small resources will be unable to follow all the lines of inquiry and will have to choose, and it is quite possible that the wrong choice will be made and a blind alley entered. But the cost, time, and performance estimates of a particular approach *improve* and become more reliable as development proceeds and new information is accumulated. The early stages of research are also comparatively cheap, and so the possibility exists of acquiring improved estimates at a reasonable cost by initiating parallel development efforts. In other words, it may be more economic *not* to choose one approach for R & D on the basis of the first estimates, which are invariably unreliable, but to pursue a multiple strategy, cutting down the list of competing projects as the estimates improve. A small firm cannot afford multiple efforts. It must choose. It may be lucky and take the right course, but experience shows that more often than not the choice based upon the uncertainties of the first estimate will be wrong, and the result, at best, will be unsatisfactory in terms of price or performance, and at worst a dead-end will be reached and work will have to begin all over again. The advantage of the large company, therefore, is that it can make use of a wider range of experts, reduce the risk by carrying a large portfolio of projects, and, in order to solve one problem, run a number of parallel projects. The chances are that they will deliver the more competitive goods – price and performance – in a shorter time. The *optimum* result *quicker*.[40]

There is no doubt whatever that the large-size American firms have significantly shorter lead times than the European companies. On average they are 20–30 per cent shorter – two years in computers and one to two in aircraft. It is therefore not altogether surprising to find that in those research-intensive industries where the life cycle of products is very short, Europe is going out of business.

Most economists now seem willing to grant that there are some important, if not crucial, advantages attached to being big in R & D, and that progress is likely to be more rapid when there are firms large enough and few enough to afford and benefit from research. At the same time, some competitive pressure is required if the results of research are to be fully and speedily utilized. The best way to organize industry is to have competition among large units – 'bigness with fewness'.[41] These conditions exist in America but not as yet in Europe.

The net result of all this is that the industrial climate in America is most conducive to rapid technological progress, and the large-scale economies in research have led to a more than proportional increase in R & D spending. The intensity of research in American industry is far higher than in European industry – about five times as great as an absolute figure or three times as large per employee. Admittedly, part of this higher intensity can be put down to the American government's heavy expenditure in the business enterprise sector. In Europe, by contrast, governments spend more of their R & D budget in their own research establishments or in the higher education and non-profit sectors. European companies also execute more of their research *externally* – probably three per cent on average – in cooperative research associations, or sponsored research organizations such as the Battelle Memorial Institutes in Frankfurt and Geneva. In the former, R & D is undertaken jointly to solve problems common to a whole industry, whereas in the latter, research is performed to meet the sponsor's individual needs and the results are confidential – the sponsor has proprietary rights. There are something like 400 cooperative research associations in Western Europe with a combined annual income (1961) of £40 million, but generally these are too small and too poor to be really effective. Nor do these arrangements have much merit when the results are shared by all competitors. In recent years the tendency has been to follow the American pattern and to do more extra-mural research in the sponsored institutes.[42] But none of this is on a scale large enough to upset the main conclusion, that due primarily to the greater size of large American firms the American worker is backed by a far more intensive and effective research effort.

Although there are certain fiscal, legal and psychological factors which inhibit the growth of European-sized companies, the main obstacle to structural change has been, and remains, the narrowness of the European domestic markets. To cite the

UNICE Report once more: 'European companies cannot be put in the dock. With few exceptions, the largest of them have reached dimensions corresponding to the size of their national markets, and they could only with difficulty base further expansion on external markets which the whim of tariff policies could close to them at any moment. It is only through consolidating a wide internal market that they can, today, formulate in new terms development policies calling for the expansion of production units, research and sales.'

Europe's limited markets create serious difficulties over lead time. The cost of developing a product is a fixed amount, independent of the number to be manufactured – an *absolute* level of resources, not a *ratio* of sales. Firms cannot afford to spend, at most, more than 10 per cent of their annual sales on R & D, so if costs are to be recovered and a profit made, out of which new research will be financed, sales must reach at least ten times the level of R & D expenditure. If it costs £20 million to develop a new computer then the annual R & D expenditure will be £20 million divided by the lead time. If the lead time is five years the annual spending is £4 million. Since sales must reach ten times the R & D expenditure, £200 million worth of computers must be sold in all, and if each computer fetches £200 000 then 1 000 must be sold. Thus the necessary cost of R & D determines the minimum level of output, and this in turn determines the minimum size of firm (as measured by sales) which will be viable. Without a market large enough to absorb 1 000 computers it would not be possible, in the above case, to stay in business.

Because research costs are a fixed amount independent of the number sold, a manufacturer with a small share of the market is automatically at a disadvantage. His profits will be low. A manufacturer with a large slice of the market will have a low research costs/sales ratio and a larger profit, but because sales are so high the manufacturer with the larger market is likely to have a much higher absolute level of R & D expenditure, for, as we have seen, by spending more it is possible to cut lead times and get results quicker. In this case it is not just a question of spending the same amount of money in a shorter space of time, it means spending more money altogether. When lead times are short, product life is short, and more generations of a particular piece of equipment will be introduced over a given period of time. The more the hurry the more the costs, and the more the costs the larger the market must be to recover the money.

In international competition speed is essential, and in order to keep abreast of the leading innovators it is necessary to make a comparable R & D effort. There is a critical 'threshold' level of R & D expenditure below which lead times become too long to survive in the race. The *time* factor accordingly pushes the necessary level of R & D effort to a new high. This will be set by the lead time of international competitors. The 'threshold' level is a purely 'defensive' position, enabling imitation of the leaders within a short time. To move on to the offensive and become a leading innovator an even greater effort is needed. In both cases the resources committed are an *absolute* level of expenditure, not a *ratio* of sales. Now, if a European company with its *small* home market, in order to keep lead times short enough to survive, brings its level of expenditure up to the 'threshold' set by an international competitor with a *large* home market, research costs are out of proportion to sales outlets, profits are cut, there is less money for future research, lead times become longer, share of the market is further diminished, and so on, until eventually the company is forced out of business, or, as is the actual case, it is taken over by its competitor who all the time has been getting stronger. But if, on the other hand, the company does not bring its spending up to the 'threshold' but chooses instead to make an effort more in proportion to the potential outlets provided by its home market, then, unless its home market is guaranteed to it, lead times become too long to survive at home and abroad. Either way the company is caught.

This is an oversimplification, but essentially it all boils down to this. In a research-intensive industry, where innovation is very rapid, it is necessary to have access to a market comparable in size to your principal competitors and this is just what European companies have not got, *vis-à-vis* the United States. One authority, in a valuable study on this problem, concluded, 'If the "threshold" set by the leading American firms for particular products is beyond the resources of individual European firms, then – barring mergers with American firms – they can only survive by rationalization of the industry either on a national or a European basis.'[43]

The size of the market exercises a powerful influence on technological progress. The intensity of research and the speed at which innovations are taken up by industry is governed by the question of profitability. Mass research requires mass production and markets if costs are to be redeemed. If the risks inherent in research are to be acceptable, a large, sophisticated, homogeneous, and, above all, an *assured* market is essential. These conditions are not found in the ordinary export trade in the world at large or in Europe. Nor are they yet satisfied within the Common Market itself.

Since the war important progress has been made in the elimination of tariffs and quotas. Inside the Common Market the setting up of the customs union has proceeded ahead of schedule and will be complete in 1968. But unfortunately the tariff wall does not constitute the most serious obstruction to goods with a high technological content. The test in buying technical goods is performance first, price second, and within reason really superior equipment rides comfortably over tariff barriers.

Behind the tariff wall there are more insidious restrictions to trade which dissever the market more thoroughly. The most serious of these, from a technological view point, are the distortions and prohibitions created by diverse patent laws, varying legal standards and technical specifications, and the discrimination practised by public buyers in the various nation states.

The territorial scope of patents runs with the national boundary. To protect inventions abroad a foreign patent must be obtained. But the procedures for granting patents and the conditions needed to qualify for patentability vary widely from one country to another. Limitations of time and use, conditions of renewal, surrender, lapse and revocation are all different, and this leads to considerable cost and delay, increasing the risks and uncertainties involved in safeguarding inventions and in recovering the costs of research. At the same time the territorial limits of patents restricts the free circulation of goods since the holder of a national patent issued by an authority in one country may prevent imports of a product from another if this infringes his patent.

Differing national standards, regulations, procedures and practices falsify, deliberately or unwittingly, competition in favour of domestic producers. Among the more serious distortions for the science-based industries are those caused by differences in technical specifications, test codes and safety provisions which are law, or are given the force of law, by national legislation, public authorities, government departents, insurance companies, standards institutes or just the convention and practice of industry itself. In the electrical industry the situation is grotesque. Apart from the problems created by varying mains voltages (standard 415/240V in Britain and 380/220V on the Continent), there are innumerable testing and approval procedures, radiation regulations, installation and shock-proofing rules, affecting creepage, clearance paths, current ratings, metric cable size of single and multiple strandcable, plugs, sockets, and the colouring of phase, neutral and earth conductors. In order to comply with these varying technical and safety regulations of the European market, manufacturers must make eleven different kinds of 60 watt incandescent lamp, five different versions of one type of heater, and twelve different versions of one type of radio.

These technical barriers to trade are just as obstructive as tariffs and are often deliberately used to maintain protection after external barriers have been removed. They vitiate competition, close markets, and make it impossible to mass-produce technically complex equipment on the scale the costs of R & D require, since production runs have to be continually interrupted to incorporate different components. All this means a diversion of technical resources to solve wholly unnecessary problems, and more talent and skill is squandered. In EFTA, despite the progressive lowering of tariffs, there has been no significant increase in the exports of electrical equipment.

The technological market in Europe is still further compartmentalized by the differing procurement methods of public buyers – governments and the agencies they fund. Governments, besides underwriting the risks of research, are very big buyers of equipment. In many cases they are an industry's principal customer. In Britain, for instance, public buyers purchase 50 per cent of the output of the construction industry, and 85 per cent of all aircraft and parts. In France and America government procurement accounts for 13 per cent and 18 per cent of the GNP. In Europe as a whole about 60 per cent (by value) of all computer installations are for state funded agencies – universities, schools, departments of state, state run banks and insurance companies, regional authorities, research centres, public utilities, etc. In America, of the total final demand, the government buys 91.4 per cent of aircraft and parts, 52.3 per cent of chemicals and chemical products, 52 per cent of electrical components and accessories, 37 per cent of scientific and controlling instruments, 22 per cent of engines and turbines, 18.9 per cent of optical and photographical equipment, and so on. The public buyer is very influential in Europe because of the size of the public sector. Almost all the transport, fuel and power, and extractive industries are in state hands, as are many banks and insurance companies. And in Italy and France the government has a sizeable stake in manufacturing industries, including mechanical engineering, electricals, and chemicals.

Now in Europe there is no equivalent of the 'Buy American' Act (1933) which obliges the Federal Government to restrict purchases to products 'mined, produced, or manufactured in the United States' even though the home bidders price may be six to twelve per cent higher (this includes transport costs) than a foreign bid, and as much as 50 per cent higher in relation

to defence spending, and for all goods for use *outside* the
United States. In practice, however, the procurement procedures that have been adopted by European governments have
an equivalent effect, fracturing the market and nullifying tariff
concessions. Indeed, they are all the more treacherous for not
being incorporated in formal legislation. For one reason or
another, strategic, social, technological, or simply because the
government has a direct interest in the industry, each grants a
'preferred' treatment to domestic suppliers over and above
normal protective measures.[44] In the interests of security and
to guarantee supplies 'buy national' preferences are common
practice in defence procurement in all countries with defence
industries. This is also true in the civil sector in some degree.
In Britain, state funded buyers must give a 25 per cent preference to home computer manufacturers. In France, Electricité
de France, as a matter of policy, will only buy French hydro-
electric plant, whatever the cost. And both British and French
airlines prefer to 'fly national' where possible. Other countries
require official contracts to be awarded to suppliers of domestic goods and for exceptions to the rule to be justified. In most
cases the discrimination against foreign goods is less open;
altogether more subtle. Procedures employed in tendering and
the attendant publicity can also be discriminatory. Automatic
tendering which is given wide publicity and where the contract
is automatically awarded to the lowest bidder, is not common
in public purchasing in Europe. More usual is the discretionary
tender which is highly selective and even secretive. The criteria
to be employed in awarding contracts are most vague, in some
cases it is the 'best bid', in others the 'most economic bid', or the
'most suitable bid', the 'most interesting bid',' the 'most advantageous from the point of view of the state bid'. There is
plenty of scope for devious construction here, and even the
'lowest bid' is not much use to the foreign supplier when his
import levy must be included in his bidding price.

All this favouritism carves up the market and research and
development remains unprofitable. In some industries both the
initial and the 'threshold' level of R & D expenditure is so great

that production is only economic when the product is taken up by the public buyer in more than one country. The aircraft industry is a perfect illustration. R & D expenditure in the aircraft industry constitutes 36 per cent of net output as against only 13 per cent in the electronics industry, and $3\frac{1}{2}$ per cent in manufacturing generally. 'The producer with the long production run has a decided advantage over the small producer. If an aircraft ... costs £25 million to develop and £1 million to produce, a manufacturer with a market of 100 could sell the aircraft at £1.25 million each and cover his costs; another manufacturer with a market of only 50 would have to charge £1.5 million each. If the development cost were no more than £5 million, or the total market sufficiently large for the sales of the two manufacturers to be 500 and 250 respectively, the selling price of the two aircraft would become £1.05 million and £1.10 million. The difference in price between them would thus become no more than £0.05 million, compared with £0.25 million in the former example.... The higher the ratio of development to production costs, the worse off is the producer with the smaller total market. By the same token, the greater will be his total and proportionate losses, if he falls short of the sales target on which he has based his price.'[45] America, with her huge, assured, home market for aircraft, has production runs for military and civil transport aircraft $4\frac{1}{2}$ times as long as ours, averaging 320 to our 68 between 1955 and 1961. As a consequence, American aircraft cost just 85 per cent of the cost of our aircraft, and their lead times are shorter. The net result of all this is that the British government contributes £127.45 million to civil aircraft and engine development between 1945 and 1965 and recovers £25.7 million by July 1965.

The position is the same, though less critical, in the other high technology industries. Small markets do not allow the high costs of R & D to be absorbed in the selling price and so long as European governments continue to buy 'national' they will find themselves shoring up industries which never pay their way, and in the meantime Europe's precious scientific resources are needlessly squandered in an endless round of dupli-

cation. In the end the position becomes untenable – as it became in the aircraft industry itself. The answer is *not* to do
away with favouritism and apply strictly commercial criteria
as the Americans proposed in the Kennedy Round – at this
stage this would simply lead to a further penetration of
American technology by virtue of the advantages American
firms enjoy in a huge home market. The answer is to coordinate
public sector purchases of high technology products on a European basis – exactly what the Plowden Committee proposed.
A discriminating use of the buying power of the state can be
a most handy tool for stimulating technological progress. The
American government has established a dynamic partnership
with industry by employing this power to reward efficiency and
penalize inefficiency. As yet no European government has learnt
to do that at a national, let alone at a European level.

*

These, then, are some of the technological facts of life. Some
of the 'reasons of scale' responsible for the technology gap. It
has been stressed, repeatedly, that bigness is not everything,
and certainly it would be an error to conclude that factors of
size alone are responsible for Europe's technological weaknesses. Nevertheless, the implications of these facts are perfectly clear – those nations who enjoy dimensions appropriate
to the 20th century are likely to progress more rapidly than
those who do not. The Common Market's Commission has
warned that if European countries should remain 'the world's
chief importers of discoveries, and primary exporters of intelligence, then they will condemn themselves to a cumulative
process of underdevelopment which sooner or later will render
their decline incurable.' A small state among small states is one
thing and a small state among large states quite another. And
if it is true – and it is true – that those countries with the power
of invention and science will win out over all others, is this not
a serious consideration for those states which rise only to the
old level of magnitude?

Chapter V

A Technological Community

In recent years an increasing awareness of the importance of science in deciding the fate of nations has precipitated a wholesale reorganization of national scientific efforts in Europe. Every country, without exception, has set about increasing the volume of its science expenditure, streamlining scientific structures, reforming procedures, and evolving a policy for science fitted to national objectives.

Britain made some major changes in 1965. Responsibility for science and technology was divided between the *Ministry of Education and Science* and the *Ministry of Technology*. The former is advised by the *Council for Scientific Policy* and has responsibility for four separate Research Councils. One of these, the *Science Research Council*, looks after grants for universities and Britain's participation in international science activities. The Ministry of Technology was established to encourage and stimulate the use of advanced technology and new processes in industry. It is assisted by a *Council for Technology*, and looks after the *Atomic Energy Authority*, the *British Standards Institution*, ten research stations, and the *National Research and Development Corporation* (NRDC). The latter was set up in 1948 to help in the development of inventions which it is in the public interest to see exploited. The new Ministry concentrated its early efforts on the computer and machine-tool industries, encouraging technological progress through civil development contracts and procurement procedures. More recently it has expanded its work into the auto-

mobile industry and aviation, having acquired responsibility
for the latter after the winding up of the Ministry of Aviation.
It has also authorized the Atomic Energy Authority to diversify
its research activities beyond the nuclear field, and enlarged the
borrowing powers of the NRDC to a £25 million ceiling.

In 1962, Britain spent 1 775 million dollars (33.5 dollars
per head) on R & D. At 2.2 per cent of the GNP this is considerably higher than any other European country. In the same year
she had 211 000 people engaged in R & D (6.1 per thousand
of the working population), and this too was considerably more
than any of her neighbours. The government was the source of
64 per cent of the funds and 63 per cent of the total scientific
effort was performed in the business enterprise sector. The
bulk of industrial research was confined to three sectors – aircraft (35.4 per cent), electrical machinery (21.7 per cent), and
chemicals (11.6 per cent).

Before the First World War *Germany's* scientific accomplish-
ment was second to none, but under the Nazis research suffered
badly. Certain branches of science were struck from the universities' curricula and many able scientists fled the country
(in 1964, thirty-six Fellows of the Royal Society were refugees
from Germany). Under the Allied Occupation several research
activities were forbidden – nuclear physics, aviation and shipbuilding research, and even after the ending of these restrictions
the bad image attached to science by the Nazis remained, re-
tarding the revival of research. In these early years financial
support came from the *Sponsor's Association* (Stifterverband),
a group of industrial organizations, and money was channelled
through the *German Research Association* (Forschungsgemein-
schaft), a non-governmental body formed by scientists themselves. 'Priority projects' were selected and money deployed
to evoke activity in neglected fields.

Under the Basic Law the freedom of research in Germany
is guaranteed and legislative competence for science is vested
jointly in the Federal and Länder (provincial) governments.
The coordination of their work has been effected by several
administrative agreements. One, signed in 1957, set up the

Scientific Council (Wissenschaftsrat), and a more general agreement to promote science and research was drawn up in 1964. The Scientific Council coordinates the plans of the Federal and Länder governments, works out the overall plan for the advancement of science, selects research priorities, and makes recommendations on the level of expenditure in various areas. In 1963, a *Federal Ministry of Scientific Research* was brought into being to centralize the nation's science policy. At present the Federal government is financially involved in five promotion programmes – space research, defence research, nuclear research for peaceful purposes, assistance for studies, and general science promotion through the extension and construction of universities. In 1966 the Federal government dispensed £237 million on research and proposes to spend £960 million in all between 1966–68, (23 per cent on defence, 19 per cent on nuclear R & D, 11 per cent on space research, and 37 per cent on general promotion).

In 1966, the gross national expenditure on research was about 2 100 million dollars of which 40 per cent was paid for by the Länder. This amounts to 1.9 per cent of the GNP (as against 1.3 per cent in 1962) and it is expected that this will climb to 3 per cent by 1970. One hundred and forty-five thousand people are engaged in R & D in all. Sixty per cent of all research was performed in the business enterprise sector, two-thirds in two sectors of industry, instruments and chemicals, and industry itself provided 60 per cent of the funds.

Belgium carried out her reorganization in 1959. A *Ministerial Committee for Science* was set up under the chairmanship of the Prime Minister. This is a decision-making and coordinating body which defines and gives effect to the country's science policy. The preparation and execution of decisions of the Ministerial Committee as they affect several departments is handled by the *Inter-ministerial Commission for Science Policy* – also created in 1959. This Commission is composed of high-level civil servants representing the departments concerned, and it is presided over by the President of the *National Council for Science Policy* (CNPS). The last-mentioned counsels the government in its elaboration of a science policy, either at the government's request or on its own initiative. It is also responsible for the country's international scientific activities which account for 10 per cent of the nation's science effort. The Council has twenty-seven members drawn from the scientific, higher education, social and economic spheres.

Belgium currently spends only 1.3 per cent of her GNP on R & D but intends to bring this up to 2 per cent by 1970 – the level projected for Europe as a whole by then. One-third of government expenditure goes on nuclear energy and space research – much of it in international organizations. Only about 40 per cent of the gross national expenditure on science is financed by the government though it is now planned to step this up to 65 per cent. The main beneficiaries of public money are the universities; only 7 per cent goes to industry and most of this to subsidize cooperative research, so 90 per cent of industrial research expenditure must be found by industry itself. Eighty-five per cent is spent in chemicals, metal-manufacturing and metallurgy. In common with other small nations Belgium's patents position is very weak. About 1.8 domestic patents are issued per ten thousand of the population as against the 12.8 per ten thousand issued to foreign applicants.

Of all the European countries *France* has made the most systematic attempt to build up her scientific and technical resources. Substantial structural changes were made in 1958. New scientific institutions have been established, an inventory taken of her research potential, the science budget greatly increased, and the quality of science teaching improved. The supreme body for science policy is the *Ministerial Committee for Scientific and Technological Research* (CIMRST), headed by the Prime Minister and composed of ten ministers representing those departments conducting research. The Committee submits proposals to the government on the development of science and coordinates the research expenditure of the various branches of government. It is assisted in its work by an *Advisory Committee for Scientific and Technological Research* (CCRST) – a group of twelve scientists chosen for their

K

competence in the scientific and technical fields, including social science, industrial and academic research. Its job is chiefly consultative although it can take limited initiatives on its own. CIMRST and the CCRST share a joint secretariat, the *General Delegation for Scientific and Technological Research* (DGRST), an organ of conception and design which conducts studies and enquiries into the development of scientific and technical research and prepares investment programmes. Two posts have been created to direct these new bodies. On the political side there is the *Secretary of State for Scientific Research and Questions of Nuclear and Space Research,* who sits on CIMRST and has separate responsibilities for the *Atomic Energy Commission* (CEA) and the *National Centre for Space Studies* (CNES). And on the scientific side there is the *Delegate-General for Scientific and Technological Research* who heads DGRST. He also sits on CIMRST.

Science planning in France is carefully coordinated with the overall objectives of the economic and social *Plan.* Under the Fifth Plan, research expenditure is to be stepped up from 1.5 per cent to 2.5 per cent of the GNP. Sixty per cent of the science budget is taken up by defence and atomic energy and the bulk of industrial research is expended on aeronautics and electrical engineering. In 1962 France spent 1 108 million dollars on R & D in all (23.6 dollars per head) and 111 200 people were occupied in science. Only 48 per cent of all research is performed in industry and the Government provides 70 per cent of the funds.

Two rather novel methods of promoting science are employed in France. One is a system of research insurance whereby the government pays for the costs of R & D on the understanding that this is repaid if the project is a commercial success. The other method is known as 'actions concertées' – combined, or interdisciplinary, research projects used on subjects which scientists feel are of particular interest and worthy of special attention. The emphasis is temporary and the projects are selected for political, economic, and social reasons, as well as for scientific motives. The arrangement enables DGRST to impart a special stimulus to the chosen sectors and to coordinate public and private research on them as closely as possible. Areas selected for combined activities under the present Plan include molecular biology, urban planning, computers, automation, water pollution and oceanography.

The overall science policy has four main aims. First, to build up the country's potential in scientists and equipment by increasing the budget appropriations for science. Second, to encourage the rapid growth of industrial research by inducing firms to devote a higher percentage of their turnover to research – the Government sharing in the risks with private firms in some fields. Third, to identify and develop certain priorities which are of great scientific and political importance, such as atomic and space research. And fourth, to make national science more effective by promoting international cooperation, thus allowing a more rational use of resources in those fields calling for efforts beyond the power of any single country of a European scale.[1]

Science in France is married to political ambition and the policy is closely linked to the theme of national independence, '. . . a scientific research policy is indispensable nowadays to a country's independence. It means independence in the widest sense i.e. the possibility for a country to raise its standard of living . . . and to have a say in the affairs of a world in which technology is becoming increasingly important: in short, not to renounce the expression of its own individual genius.'[2] There is great concern at the country's growing dependence on American know-how. None of France's major industries are able to balance their patent accounts and for every one hundred national patents taken out, 170 are issued to foreign applicants. There are only six research workers for every ten thousand citizens compared to the twenty-three for every ten thousand in America, and the United States spends fifty-four times as much as France on aeronautics and 135 times as much on electrical engineering. Quite how the national aspiration of independence is compatible with the necessity, which is recognized, of international collaborbation has never been explained.[3 & 4]

These efforts at the national level are all very gratifying, but if European science is to be rejuvenated and the technology gap closed these efforts must be reinforced by vigorous action at the international level, aimed firstly to prevent wasteful duplication of research work, and aimed secondly to provide the market/industrial conditions more favourable to the exploitation of inventions. Here too, some progress has been recorded.

BILATERAL ACCORDS

France, despite, or perhaps because of, the strong nationalistic tone of her policy has recognized more quickly and more thoroughly than others the necessity for countries of average dimensions to complement their own scientific efforts with international programmes. However, in order to guarantee 'independence' the policy seems to be to conclude these arrangements between as many countries as possible. France now collaborates with America in space research – the French satellite FR 1 was launched by the United States, with Britain and Germany in aircraft development and production, and with the Soviet Union in the Secam system of colour TV – the Russian Molniya satellite has been used to relay colour TV between Moscow and Paris. Additionally, under an agreement signed in Moscow in June 1966, Russia and France are to cooperate in space research, meteorology and telecommunications. This agreement includes earth satellite communications and the launching of a French satellite by a Soviet space rocket.[5] There have been talks on joint aircraft production, and these two countries already work together on high energy physics. France is installing a liquid-hydrogen bubble chamber at Serpukhov where the Soviets are completing their 70 GeV proton accelerator. There is also an older Franco-Russian agreement to combine research activities on cancer, leukaemia, molecular biology, neuro-physiology and oceanography. This provides for the exchange of experts for substantial periods, and the mutual communication of results of work conducted in parallel.

Bilateral accords of one kind and another are widespread in Europe. The process has been carried furthest in the aircraft industry where apart from international project collaboration there is also a fair degree of international specialization. There are some fifty major international programmes underway at present; British aerospace companies alone have thirty agreements with other European companies and the French aircraft industry reckons that Anglo-French projects will soon account for 80 per cent of their entire activities. This partnership already amounts to £1 500 million worth of research and development – £500 million for the *Concorde* supersonic airliner, £300 million for the Anglo-French *Variable Geometry Aircraft* (AFVG), £200 million for the *Jaguar* strike/trainer aircraft, £190 million for the medium haul *Airbus* project, £50 million for the highly successful *Martel* advanced air-to-ground missile, which links Hawker Siddeley Dynamics-Engins Matra-Dassault-Nord Aviation, and £40 million for three types of helicopter, the *SA 330*, the *SA 340* and the *WG 13*, to be produced by Sud-Aviation and Westlands.

The *Concorde* agreement, signed in November 1962, is the most ambitious of these projects. The British Aircraft Corporation (BAC) are working together with Sud-Aviation on the airframe, while Bristol Siddeley and SNECMA work on the engines. After modifications to the original design the plane will now carry 136–140 passengers and fly at Mach 2.2 (1 450 mph). Two prototypes are being built. The first is due to fly in February 1968 and deliveries should commence in 1971. The costs of development have soared from an original estimate of £150 millions to £500 millions and they will go still higher. The market for these planes is put at 200 plus, and so far delivery positions have been reserved for seventy-four. Commercial success will depend ultimately on *Concorde* holding its three year lead over the American counterpart. BAC and Sud-Aviation are each responsible for various bits and pieces of the airframe and there are two assembly lines, one at Toulouse, France, and the other at Filton, England. The overall project is controlled by an Anglo-French ministerial committee of officials advised by a technical committee.

The *Jaguar* is a light supersonic (Mach 1.8) strike/trainer plane, BAC and Breguet building the airframe, and Rolls Royce and Turboméca the engines. A prototype is due to fly in 1968 and the aircraft will enter service with the Armée de l'Air and the RAF in the early 1970's. The memorandum of understanding on this plane was initialled in May 1965, and a special Anglo-French company was formed (SEPECAT) to design and produce it. The AFVG plane is to be produced by BAC and Dassault, and Bristol Siddeley and SNECMA. It is to be suitable for strike, interception and reconnaissance.*

These joint projects have not been without their difficulties. The political and defence policies of the two countries are still too far apart to draft long-range programmes in the military or civilian fields. At present, collaboration involves long delay while ways are found to reconcile the different operational requirements created by the varying defence philosophies. There have been misgivings over the cost inflation and over the inadequate means of controlling the finance of international projects. The duplication of tooling can be avoided to some extent by the interchange of components but the problems inherent in building in two separate countries at once, due in part to the necessity of transporting various parts between them, increases the cost by some 25 per cent. Ideally, it would be best for each country to make different aircraft separately and then secure an adequate market by agreeing to exchange the final product, but this implies a degree of political mutuality which these nations do not seem prepared to accept. Even so, the advantages of cooperation are considerable. Skilled manpower and development costs are shared and the potential market is at least doubled in bilateral projects. In this respect (despite the view that costs increase in direct ratio to the number of partners) multilateral cooperation would be even more advantageous. The most likely partner is Germany. The Germans were in fact invited to join the discussions on a supersonic airliner in the mid-1950's, but showed no interest. But

* Now cancelled.

Germany was a member of the continental European consortium, NASMO, (with Holland, Italy and Belgium) which produced the American *Starfighter* under licence, and she also cooperated with France on the *Transall* transport aircraft. It is still possible that she will come in on the AFVG project, and she will certainly be participating in the *Airbus* project – although a final decision on this plane has yet to be made. It is planned that Hawker Siddeley, Sud-Aviation and a West German airbus group should work on the airframe, and Rolls Royce, SNECMA and MAN Turbomotoren on the engines. One problem about wholehearted German participation in European aircraft projects is the sizeable American interest in the German aircraft industry. Boeing have a one-third interest in Bölkow, and the United Aircraft Corporation a 26 per cent interest in Vereinigte Flugwerk.

Outside of the aircraft industry there was another proposal for Anglo-French cooperation – to build a giant computer. This was to be ten times as powerful as anything yet made and would have cost £12 million to develop. The idea was first mooted in July 1965 when it was planned that ICT, English Electric and CITEC of France should combine to develop it; but the project seems to have been shelved while the French computer industry reorganizes what is left of itself. Although the market for such a machine is uncertain the two British companies may now go it alone. When this proposal was made there was also a lot of talk of ICT, CITEC and Telefunken of Germany banding together to form a large European consortium to meet American competition. This too seems to have come to nothing.

MULTILATERAL COOPERATION

International cooperation in science is nothing new. There has been a genuine scientific community in Europe since the Renaissance and in the 18th century joint observations and experiments were being performed internationally. Common research programmes multiplied in the last century. Astronomers in different countries combined to map the sky and by the 1880's this work occupied eighteen national observatories in the northern hemisphere. Congresses were held to provide regular contacts and from these originated, as more permanent bureaux, the first international scientific organizations. They were all founded on the initiative of scientific circles although governments sometimes took a hand in negotiating the agreement. The *International Bureau of Weights and Measures* (1875) is the best known of these early institutions. For a long time it was distinguished for being the only one with its own research facilities. By 1914 there were something like fifty-three international science organizations of one kind and another – governmental and non-governmental. After the war the movement intensified so that by 1939 a further forty-three organizations had been added to the list. Amongst these should be mentioned the *International Council of Scientific Unions* (ICSU) which superseded the International Research Council in 1931. It was founded to facilitate and coordinate the activities of the various international scientific unions and the work of the national academies and societies of member states. In recent years ICSU has had financial assistance from UNESCO and was responsible for organizing the *International Geophysical Year* and the *Year of the Quiet Sun* involving joint observations in more than sixty countries.

The chief purpose of these organizations was to facilitate international contacts, and promote the exchange of information and the dissemination of research results. Few were involved in planning common research programmes nor did they carry out research work of their own. There were two exceptions: the *Naples Zoological Station* (1870) and the *Jüngfraujoch Scientific Station* (1931) in Switzerland. These were true international facilities which supplied equipment and laboratories for individual research workers for the payment of a fee.

Since 1945, the aims and methods of international cooperation in science have altered radically. Cooperation is no longer confined to consultation and to the exchange of research results but extends to the joint conduct of large-scale research projects, government-financed and often government-inspired, involving large numbers of personnel and expensive equipment. International cooperation in science has now become an instrument of political, economic, social and military policy. Sometimes governments have backed international scientific activities for prestige reasons, or because they contributed to wider political and economic objectives, but more usually they have done so because the research in question was by its very nature transnational in scope – oceanography, meteorology, radio-astronomy; or because it called for resources in men, materials and money on a scale beyond the means of single countries – space research and nuclear research. Today there are about 250 nongovernmental and fifty intergovernmental organizations engaged in scientific activities.[6]

Among international organizations that have been concerned with the promotion of science and technology in Europe since the last war, although their aims are not essentially scientific, are the *North Atlantic Treaty Organization* (NATO), and the *Organization for Economic Cooperation and Development* (OECD). NATO has a *Committee of Defence Research Directors* which deals with cooperation in defence research, but there is also a *Science Committee* presided over by an *Assistant Secretary-General for Scientific Affairs* which promotes a modest civilian research programme with the rather ambitious aim of building up the general scientific strength of the Alliance. The promotion takes the form of financial assistance for science fellowships, research grants, and the organization of Advanced Study Institutes (summer schools). Under the fellowship programme post-graduates are enabled to work in other countries. Research grants are used to finance cooperative international projects (these absorb 85 per cent of the grants) as well as purely national projects. Oceanography has received special attention. NATO also runs a *Training Centre for Experimental Aerodynamics*, taken over from the United States and Belgium in 1961. The total science appropriations of the Treaty Organization runs at 4 million dollars a year and the bulk is spent on the science fellowships scheme. NATO also sponsored the *Armand Committee* on ways of increasing the effectiveness of Western science, and the *Killian Committee* on a proposal for an *International Institute of Science and Technology* which was to provide post graduate research and teaching facilities. This came to nothing.[7]

The work of OECD has been most important. The scientific activities of the Organization are based on Article 2(b) of the Convention: 'Members are agreed that they will, both individually and jointly ... in the scientific and technological fields, promote the development of their resources, encourage research ...' The activities are carried out under the aegis of the *Committee for Scientific Research* (CSR) and the *Committee for Scientific and Technical Personnel* (CSTP). The first is responsible for the activities of the Organization in the field of science, and the second is responsible for work relating to the expansion and rational use of the available scientific and technical personnel as well as for the policies for scientific training. There is also a *Directorate of Scientific Affairs* with four divisions, and to this is attached the *Central Service for International Cooperation in Scientific Research.*

The general aim of developing the scientific resources of member states has been furthered in two ways; through the promotion and harmonization of national science policies, as a result of which some valuable studies on individual country's scientific organization and policy, and the collation of badly needed statistics, have been made; and through the promotion of scientific research at an international level. OECD has no research establishments of its own and a functional method of cooperation is employed. International research programmes are established on restricted topics between the scientific institutes of different countries wishing to collaborate, each country taking responsibility, in ideal circumstances, for one part of the total programme. The Organization does not itself contribute to the R & D costs, which are financed severally by the participating countries, but only pays for the promotional expenses of rendering them international. The advantage of this method is that it involves no new international installations.

The fields covered under his procedure have been common problems like road safety, production engineering, marine corrosion, pollution, noise, desalting, metal fatigue, etc.

For some years OECD have been doing some exploratory work on industrial research management and on means of collaboration between firms in European member countries. From this work has emerged a new autonomous body, set up in May 1966, with its own governing council – the *European Industrial Research Management Association* (EIRMA). The Association aims to study the organization of industrial research, scientific research and technological development, and to examine economic and effective methods of managing research in Europe.

OECD also has a specialized agency, the *European Nuclear Energy Agency* (ENEA), whose aim is to foster the production and use of nuclear energy for peaceful purposes by cooperation and harmonization of measures taken at a national level. It has no research establishments of its own. It acts as an initiating agency, fostering the creation of research establishments by means of joint undertakings, and it also seeks to harmonize legislation relating to nuclear energy in Europe. There are three important joint undertakings: the Norwegian heavy boiling water reactor project at Halden; the experimental Dragon high temperature reactor at Winfrith Heath, Britain; and the Eurochemic nuclear fuel processing plant at Mol, Belgium. These three projects, involving a total investment of over 120 million dollars, employ more than 500 scientists and engineers. The *Halden* project, costing 11.8 million dollars, involves eleven nations in an undertaking that has run for nine years. The reactor, which has been operational since 1959, was originally used for experiments but is now employed as an irradiation testing facility for prototype power reactor fuel elements. The *Dragon* project links twelve nations (the EURATOM Commission and the UKAEA are the main partners) in an eight-year experiment costing 70 million dollars. The reactor went critical in 1964 and reached its full design output of 20 MW (th) in April 1966. The HTGR system has so far proved so successful that it is claimed that it will generate electricity as cheaply as fast breeders – the 'third generation' of reactors. *Eurochemic*, the European Company for the Chemical Processing of Irradiated Fuels, is an international shareholding company which remains under government control through the Special Group of the Steering Committee of ENEA. It associates thirteen countries and signed its first contracts for reprocessing in 1965.

The *European Organization for Nuclear Research* (CERN) is generally accepted as the most successful international scientific organization. It was set up in 1953 on the initiative of a small group of scientists with the support of UNESCO. It is, however, an intergovernmental body, and conducts research on sub-nuclear physics. It is not concerned with military work or with activities related to nuclear energy applications, but only with research of a purely scientific and fundamental character. There are at present two major experimental facilities; the 600 MeV (million electron volts) synchro-cyclotron commissioned in 1957, and the £9 million 28 GeV proton synchrotron operational since 1959. This machine is now to be enhanced by the addition of intersecting storage rings. It already ranks as the third largest accelerator in the world after the 33 GeV machine at Brookhaven in America, and the 70 GeV machine at Serpurkhov in Russia. There is the proposal that CERN should have a 300 GeV machine costing £150 million to be sited in a new location. A decision on this is imminent. America is just about to start building a 200 GeV accelerator near Chicago. The CERN centre at Meyrin, Geneva, employs 300 scientists and engineers, and 800 technicians, and has a budget of £14 million which is increasing by 12 per cent a year. Costs are apportioned according to the national incomes of the thirteen member states, Britain paying about 22 per cent of the total. CERN is free to buy equipment where it pleases and tends to buy the best equipment available, irrespective of price or source. This explains the high value of purchases from the United States. Britain gets only 5 per cent of the orders.

The *European Atomic Energy Community*, generally known as EURATOM, is the organization of the Six in the nuclear sphere. The Treaty came into force in January 1958 for an unlimited duration. Its purpose is 'to contribute to raising the standard of living in Member States and to the development of commercial exchanges with other countries by the creation of conditions necessary for the speedy establishment and growth of nuclear industries'. In particular, to develop research and ensure the dissemination of technical knowledge, to establish uniform safety standards and facilitate investment, to ensure the construction of basic facilities and the supply of ores and nuclear fuels, and to create a common market for specialized plant and equipment by the free movement of capital for nuclear investment, and by the freedom of employment for specialists within the Community.

EURATOM's has functioned primarily as a research and development organization, supplementing the efforts of member countries through a Community research programme and coordinating public and private research activities at the national level. The research programme has three major lines of action: the development of various types of reactor, proven and new, and research in connection with fuel cycles: the study of controlled thermo-nuclear reaction: research on the effects of radiation and their application in medicine, industry and agriculture. Research is carried out in three ways: by contracts with industry and research institutions, of limited scope and duration and wholly financed by EURATOM; by 'association contracts' – a formula which enables work done under national programmes to be put on a Community basis by the participation of EURATOM. In this case the two parties share the costs; and thirdly, in EURATOM's own *Joint Research Centre* (JRC) to which half the total budget is allocated. The Centre has four separate establishments. *Ispra*, in northern Italy, is the largest with a staff of 1 700. The main work here is the *Orgel* project involving research on natural uranium-fuelled atomic reactors using heavy water as a moderator and an organic liquid as a coolant. A critical assembly, ECO, part of the project, is in operation and a test reactor ESSOR (25 MW) has recently been completed. Also located at Ispra is a *Scientific Information Processing Centre* (CETIS), with IBM 360, IBM 1401 and 7090 computers. Research is also done here on nuclear physics, reactor physics, fuel chemistry, solid state physics, direct conversion, and biology. *Petten*, in the north of Holland, is a general purpose establishment. It employs 300 people. The main feature is a materials testing high-flux reactor (HFR) of the tank-pool type. *Geel*, in Belgium, is the location of the *Central Nuclear Measurement Bureau* (CNMB), a specialized laboratory for standardizing and perfecting nuclear measurements. The Bureau has a van de Graff particle accelerator and employs 180 people. The fourth establishment of the JRC is the *European Transuranium Institute*, sited in *Karlsruhe*, Germany, and opened in 1965. The Institute is concerned with transuranium elements and plutonium-based fuel elements. An important part of its work consists of studying the recycling of plutonium in reactors. The Institute will eventually have a staff of 300.

Association contracts cover long-term, large-scale research projects. Joint research teams are established under the direction of a joint management. Through this formula EURATOM has been able to prevent wasteful duplication by coordinating and rationalizing programmes carried out within the member states. Association contracts account for about 35 per cent of research expenditure and include five contracts for fast-breeder reactor development and six for thermonuclear research. The Community accounts for about 19 per cent of the world's work on fusion research against 12 per cent by the UK, 25 per cent by the US, and 35 per cent by the USSR. Most of EURATOM's work on ship propulsion is being performed under association contracts. This includes backing for the German nuclear-powered ship, the *Otto Hahn*. The Community contributed four million dollars towards the cost of its reactor.

Two hundred and fifteen million dollars were allocated for EURATOM's first five-year research programme (1958–63) during which something like 300 ordinary and association contracts were signed. Under the second five-year programme (1963–68), which was revised in May 1965, 430.58 million dollars were allocated for research, plus 25.8 million dollars left over from the first programme. 238.3 million dollars were granted for reactor and associated research including 64 million dollars for the *Orgel* project. 153.5 million dollars were granted to the JRC, 83.3 million to faster breeder development, 34 million on fusion studies and 6 million on marine propulsion.

Currently, nuclear power stations produce 3 per cent of the Community's electricity. A target programme has been published indicating that the Community should have installed nuclear capacity of 4 000 MW by 1970, 12 000 MW by 1975, 40 000 MW by 1980, and 370 000 MW by the end of the century. It was estimated that between 1980 and 2000 two-thirds of new power station capacity would be nuclear. The total cost of all plant to be installed between now and the close of the century is put at £21 500 million. This projection was calculated on the assumption that only 'proven-type' reactors would be installed before 1975. And after that advanced-converters, such as the *Orgel* or *Dragon* type reactor, would be used until fast breeders took over from 1980 onwards.

A common market for all nuclear materials and equipment, involving a low common external tariff and internal free trade, has been in operation since 1959, and a regulation providing for the free movement of atomic workers is in force. Progress has also been made in standardizing health, safety and nuclear insurance regulations. The Community has also developed links with third countries, the United States in particular. Although EURATOM is the extension and instrument, in the nuclear sphere, of European economic integration its powers on the industrial side are rather meagre. It is not its task, for instance, to build power-stations. Even so, by providing investment aid – 32 million dollars allocated from the research fund, the Community is participating in the construction of six major power plants in member states under the Power Reactor Participation Programme. Three of these are being carried out in conjunction with the United States under the Joint Power Programme –

the Italian SENN 150 MW project near Naples, the Franco-Belgium SENA group's 266 MW project in the French Ardennes, and the German KRB group's 237 MW plant near Ulm. Four projects have been granted what is known as 'Joint-Enterprise' status. This arrangement gives certain fiscal and customs advantages to the constructor in return for constructional and operating information.

The budget of the Community is financed by member countries but there are different scales for the research and investment budget and the working budget. The Treaty provides for the eventual replacement of this method of financing by Community funding from the proceeds of levies.[8]

The *European Coal and Steel Community* (ECSC) also has a research programme. Under Article 55 of the Treaty 'The High Authority shall encourage technical and economic research concerning the production and the development of consumption of coal and steel as well as labour safety in these industries. To this end, it shall establish all appropriate contacts among existing research organizations.' The ECSC has no research establishments of its own but encourages technical research, both fundamental and applied, on coal and steel by subsidizing research under contract in public, private, university and industrial research institutes in member states. In its first ten years of operation the Community devoted 31.9 million dollars to research. Research appropriations have been stepped up in the last few years and in 1966 8.7 million dollars were spent, bringing the total research expenditure of the Community since 1952 to 83.1 million dollars – 24.8 million for steel, 23.3 million for coal, 7.2 million for minerals and 27.6 for social research. Work has been undertaken in automation and labour-saving methods, steel production techniques including continuous steel casting, industrial health and medicine, and work safety. The Community's financing represents only 4 per cent of all steel research expenditure in the member countries, and 15 per cent in the case of coal. Small as this is, the use of common funds has made it possible in some degree to coordinate research to avoid wasteful duplication and has enabled research projects to be undertaken which were too large for any one firm, or even any national research institute, to finance and carry on on its own. Unlike other international organizations the ECSC's budget is not financed by member governments but by a tax levied on all coal and steel production.[9]

Space research is a new area for European collaboration. The *European Space Research Organization* (ESRO) was brought into existence in March 1964, as the result of an initiative by the same group of scientists who took part in creating CERN. The Organization exists to provide for and promote collaboration among European States in space research and technology – exclusively for peaceful purposes. Its aims are purely scientific. It is not concerned with launching vehicles, manned flights or satellite communications. Six establishments are being set up: the *European Space Technology Centre* (ESTEC) in the Netherlands with the task of designing, developing, constructing nose cones and satellites; to this centre is attached the *European Space Laboratory* (ESLAB); the *European Space Data Centre* (ESDAC) in Germany handles the reception and analysis of information; the *European Space Research Institute* (ESRIN) in Italy is a laboratory for advanced scientific research; the *European Space Tracking System* (ESTRACK) has four stations dotted around the world – in Alaska, Spitzbergen, the Falkland Islands, with the main centre at Redu, Belgium; and finally the *European Space Launching Range* (ESRANGE) at Kiruna, Sweden – a launching site for sounding rockets.

The Organization acts as a supplier of facilities, placing its laboratories and equipment at the disposal of scientists from the universities and institutions of member states. For the most part the experiments are conceived, built and carried through nationally by universities and government establishments. There is a £110 million budget for the first eight years and contributions are apportioned between the ten member states according to national incomes; Britain currently pays

L

25 per cent. The Organization will eventually have a staff of 1 400.

The programme of ESRO includes launching sounding rockets (forty a year carrying seventy experiments) to study the ionosphere and ultra-violet radiation; putting in orbit small satellites for radio-astronomic researches and for magnetic and geodesic measurements; sending probes into space to explore the distant regions of the solar system; and placing astronomical observatories around the earth and moon. The first two satellites, ESRO I and II, were to be launched free of charge by the Americans in 1967, the first to study high altitude energetic particles, and the second carrying experiments of Britain, France and Holland, to study solar radiation and cosmic rays. The Large Astronomical Satellite (LAS), for which Britain has won the contract, is due to be launched in 1971 – probably on ELDO's *Europa I.*

The *European Space Vehicle Launcher Development Organization* (ELDO) came into being in February 1964 as the result of an initiative by the British government who were seeking a peaceful use for their *Blue Streak* rocket, developed for strategic purposes. The objectives of the Organization are to develop and construct space vehicle launchers and their equipment suitable for practical applications and for supply to eventual users. ELDO links six European countries and Australia. All the European members also belong to ESRO and close cooperation between the two organizations is planned. The desirability of a merger between them has been considered. The Organization uses existing facilities as far as possible and can supply launchers for non-members. Technological information from the programme can be communicated to all member states without payment, subject to certain conditions, whenever it is to be used for purposes outside the field of space technology.

The initial five-year programme of ELDO was to develop a three-stage rocket, *Europa I* (ELDO A), which was to be capable of putting scientific satellites into low orbit: Britain to provide the first stage, France the second, and Germany the third, while Italy was to construct the first series of experimental satellites, Belgium the down-range guidance stations and the Netherlands the long range telemetry links. Australia was to supply the launching site. The first firing of the complete rocket with satellite was originally fixed for September 1966, but by January of that year ELDO had run into serious difficulties. The project had slipped three years behind schedule, costs had escalated from £70 million to £158 million, and the project as it stood had been overtaken by events and served no obvious purpose. In particular, it was not powerful enough to place communications satellites in orbit. The biggest single factor in upsetting the programme was the delay in ratifying the Treaty. However, the programme has now been revamped. It has been decided to go ahead with the intial programme which should be complete by 1969, but at the same time the launcher is to be upgraded by the addition of a perigee-apogee propulsion system (ELDO PAS) which will enable ELDO to place 110 lb communications satellites into 24 hour 'synchronous' orbit from an equatorial launching site – French Guiana. The latest estimate for the initial and PAS programme is £224 million. At the end of 1966 £106 million of this had already been spent and a ceiling of £118 million has been placed on expenditure between 1967–71. In 1966 the scale of national contributions were also revised more equitably, Britain's share being cut from almost 39 per cent to 27 per cent of the costs.[10]

These are the main international organizations currently engaged in scientific and technological collaboration in Europe. There are others. The *European Molecular Biology Organization* (EMBO), a non-governmental undertaking formed by scientists from ten countries and providing research grants and advanced training for young scientists. It hopes to set up an international laboratory to provide all the elaborate apparatus this interdisciplinary subject requires – X-ray diffraction analysers, culture systems, electron microscopes, automatic chemical analysers, computers and so forth. Then there is the *International Computation Centre* in Rome, and the *International Centre for Theoretical Physics* in Trieste, sponsored by the Italian government, and the *International Atomic Energy*

Agency in Vienna. And at the industrial level there are numerous industrial liaison groups like *Eurospace* and *Foratom*.

The extent of collaboration seems impressive and it appears as though Europe has already gone some way towards pooling her intellectual resources and avoiding duplication of effort. But the picture is misleading. To begin with none of this is yet on a scale great enough to redress the balance between Europe and America. International research projects barely account for 4 per cent of Western Europe's scientific effort, although in some areas they do represent a much higher proportion of the total. Nuclear and space research, for instance, account for 50 per cent and 30 per cent, respectively, of all international spending on science. But even EURATOM's research budget equals only 20 per cent of the Community's entire effort in this sphere. In space research it is true that international projects absorb as much as 65 per cent of the whole, but in this case the overall outlay is so puny as to make no difference. In 1965, Europe spent about £65 million on space research as against £2 400 and £2 250 millions spent by America and Russia respectively. Thus with a population half as big again as America's and with the combined GNPs of European states equalling two-thirds that of America, Western European space spending, in absolute terms, is only one-fortieth that of the United States. There are independent national programmes in space of varying scale. France has an ambitious satellite launching programme on which she spends £23 million a year (75 per cent of her space spending goes on national projects). Britain spends £16 million (only about 12 per cent on national projects), and Germany spends £17 million (30 per cent on national projects). The international, national and bilateral agreements are only very loosely coordinated. There have been calls for a long-term, clearly defined, European space programme directed by a European Space Authority, comparable to NASA, bringing together ESRO, ELDO, and CETS (Conférence Européenne sur Télécommunications par Satellite) – a committee which represents European interests in the world communications system, *Intelsat*. Nothing has come of this idea however.

Another factor working against the effectiveness of these organizations is the fact that they have no authority over
national programmes. Progress is dependent on national policies and member states quite naturally give priority to their
own projects over the common programme. Participation in
international ventures is directed towards supplementing and
reinforcing their own science potential. There is no permanent
fusion but limited collaboration for a limited time in sectors
of joint importance, covering research and investment which
go beyond national programmes by reasons of their costs, risks
and importance. Indeed, countries will only agree to join in on
international projects when they themselves do research in related fields since this is the only way they can take advantage
of the experiments and experience gained on an international
basis. As a result the coordination of national research programmes has met with very limited success, and member
countries continue to compete with one another in parallel
activities. What is worse many of the international organizations are also duplicating each other's work in similar if not
identical fields, and there is much overlapping. Competition in
research is beneficial up to a point but over multiplication is
wasteful. Anyhow, European countries have enough to do
competing with America without competing between themselves.

Nor have these international organizations been all that they
might have been. Governments have dithered about, chopping
and changing budgets and programmes, adding to the uncertainties of research. Confidence and stability are essential in
scientific programmes. In the absence of a guarantee of continuity in the scale of effort and of stability in the provision
of finance, it is impracticable to apply sound planning and
management techniques; hard to attract scientists and technologists of adequate calibre into the organization; difficult to per-
suade industry to participate wholeheartedly in the enterprise;
and impossible to pursue scientific investigations of any real
significance.

Other problems have arisen over the unequal level of

scientific attainment in member nations, and over languages, variations in technical specifications and legal standards, patents rights, and red-tape, all of which are as nothing compared to the difficulties caused by divergent national interests. The importance of the results of research for defence and commerce impede the free and full exchange of information and the pooling of research results, and this has made it hard to build really effective common organizations. That is why intellectual collaboration has proved more fruitful than material collaboration. As science is becoming more highly valued as a national resource the problems of collaboration are becoming more serious. Governments are demanding a return for their money in proportion to their outlay which defeats the whole object of cooperation. According to the Director-General of ESRO '. . . the best way of "selling" the scheme to the Chanceries of Europe originally was by emphasizing that there would be valuable feedbacks from ESRO contracts to the national economies'. Something for everybody in the division of research projects is a bad philosophy. Ideally, money should be provided by each country according to capacity, and contracts should be awarded according to competence. It would possibly be better to agree on a division of labour between various projects rather than within one project.

Research at the international level in Europe then is far from satisfactory. Dr King of OECD has summed up the position, '. . . the basic overheads of science have to be met separately by each state, with the result that there is much useless duplication and sub-threshold effort. The situation is much the same as if, in the United States, each state of the union were to attempt individually to provide the whole apparatus of the contemporary scientific effort.'[11] And on top of all this Europe has still to provide herself with market and industrial conditions favourable to technological progress.

THE MARKET/INDUSTRIAL BASE

The European market, for all the progress in eliminating tariffs and quotas, remains fragmented because legal barriers have become economic frontiers, preventing concentration between firms in different countries, foiling mass production according to uniform standards, and impeding the exploitation and protection of inventions. An enlarged and strengthened Common Market has the potential to create standards of size more favourable to technological progress but for the moment it remains too disserved and weak for research, particularly in the high technologies, to be economically worthwhile. The intensity of research remains below the level necessary to meet international competition. This is due, let us remind ourselves, to the wide variations in technical and quality standards, the existence of different patent legislation in each country, the absence of any joint procurement system by public buyers, and the presence of a large number of small firms unable to afford the critical 'threshold' size of R & D effort needed to match external competitors. Progress within the Common Market in eliminating these non-tariff obstacles to development has been less than satisfactory, although now that the customs union is virtually complete these problems are receiving more attention.

In the Common Market technical barriers to trade are to be done away with since the Rome Treaty makes the harmonization of legislative and administrative provisions obligatory when they have a direct incidence on the establishment and functioning of the Common Market. So far the Commission have tackled technical barriers affecting pressure vessels, electrical domestic appliances, electrical installations and machinery, tractors, agricultural machinery, motor vehicles, measuring and weighing instruments, pipelines and portable tools. But progress in applying common standards has been ever so slow. The Commission have also published a recommendation that member states should take care to avoid creating new obstacles to trade when adopting laws and regulations of a technical nature, and so as to help prevent intra-Community trade from being hampered by new, divergent technical arrangements members are requested to notify the Commission of changes before legal enactment.

Standardization, of course, goes on outside the Common

Market – but without the force of law. The *International Standardization Organization* (ISO) promotes the development of common standards so as to facilitate the international exchange of goods and services, and helps to develop cooperation in the sphere of intellectual, scientific, technological and economic activity. The *International Electrotechnical Commission* (IEC) is an autonomous division of the ISO, solely concerned with electrical matters. It strives to create common terminologies, testing methods, dimensions and other specifications that affect trade exchanges. There is also the *International Commission on Rules for the Approval of Electrical Equipment* (CEE) which bases its standards primarily on German specifications. EFTA tends to accept standards set down by existing standards bodies, but in order to harmonize the activities of the Six and the Seven the *European Standards Coordination Committee* (CEN) has been set up together with the *European Electrical Standards Coordination Committee* (CENEL). Both are trying to get the thirteen countries to introduce standards already agreed. The *European Computer Manufacturers Association* (ECMA) has done valuable work in its own field coordinating and devising at an international level standards in computer operating techniques, programming languages, input-output codes, etc. All these bodies have done sterling work but it is unfortunate that their proposals are not binding. Some countries enforce the recommendations and others do not. At the same time the national standards institutes busy themselves with new recommendations made with scant regard to what other nations are doing. The net effect is to increase the total number of standards in force.[12] All have to be complied with when exporting to another country. A far more vigorous and systematic attack against technical obstacles to trade will be needed if the problem is not to become more intractable and if a split between the Six and the others in Europe is to be avoided.

There is no direct reference in the Rome Treaty to industrial property, but Article 36 excludes the protection of industrial property from the operation of Articles 30 to 34 which provide for the mutual liberalization of restrictions – but only on the condition that this protection is not made a means of arbitrary discrimination or a disguised restriction on trade between members. To secure the free movement of goods the harmonization of patent law is essential and the Commission have made some proposals. Two possibilities have been considered; a Community patent involving the creation of a single patent for the Six, exclusive to member states with special provisions to associate non-members; and an International patent involving as many countries as possible. This system would be limited in substance to setting up a uniform procedure for the grant of patents, giving the patentee not a single patent as under the Community system proposed, but a bunch of national patents. The Commission preferred the Community patent idea for political and practical reasons. First, it was considered an important factor making for integration of the Six. Second, it could be set up quicker which was important in view of the pressing need to provide uniform protection throughout an area becoming economically more and more united. Moreover, a Community patent would not require new institutions, other than a Community patent office, since the existing institutions of the Community could supervise and operate the system. A single patent for the whole Community territory would allow patented products to circulate freely. In the Commission's view this system was the only one compatible with complete economic union since it would prevent the patentee or licensee from splitting up the operation of the patent or licence within the Common Market. An international patent on the other hand, although it would help to avoid a split between the Six and the rest, suffered from the disadvantage that the legal provisions regarding a patent once issued would be left to the legislative and judicial interpretation of the individual member states. A single procedure for granting international patents would not prevent each national patent from being assigned, licensed or revoked in complete independence of one another.

Discussions on the patent question has been going on in the Community since 1959, and in 1961 the Commission published

a Draft Convention on the subject, providing for a single Community patent capable of existing alongside national patents.
It would confer on the owner of a patent exclusive rights in the
whole of the territories of member states and would only be
negotiable in respect of the whole territory. It would not be
possible to hold a Community patent and a national patent at
the same time. The Draft also provided that in the case of non-
development or insufficient development in relation to the
needs of all the states, compulsory licences to work the invention could be granted. But this Convention has not even been
approved let alone implemented.[13]

Articles 12 to 29 of the Treaty establishing EURATOM
deal with patent rights in this special sphere. In contracts of
association and in contracts with professional research institutes, which normally leave title to patents to contractors,
patent rights are settled on a contract by contract basis.
But in ordinary contracts the contractor is entitled to the
patent rights in all countries if he desires, but if he waives
the right or abandons the patent after the grant, then the
Community has the right to file the patent application and
maintain it for its own benefit. In this case the contractor
retains a royalty-free, non-exclusive licence. In any event the
Community disposes of a royalty-free licence for its own purposes and the Commission can grant sub-licences to member
states for use with nuclear applications; if the information is to
be used for research purposes only, however, there is no restriction on the uses.

The Rome Treaty is silent on the question of public purchasing but there are a number of general provisions that can
be interpreted as forbidding favouritism in public buying
methods where these distort intra-Community trade. Article
92, for instance, states that '... any aid, granted by a Member
State or granted by means of state resources, in any manner
whatsoever, which distorts or threatens to distort competition
by favouring certain enterprises or certain productions shall,
to the extent to which it adversely affects trade between Member

States, be deemed to be incompatible with the Common Market'.

The most the EEC Commission has done is to issue a directive on the coordination of public works contracts in excess of 300 000 dollars. Up to the end of the transitional period, public works contracts awarded by gas, water and electricity supply undertakings operated directly by the state or local authorities are excluded from the scope of the directive, while contracts awarded by public rail, road and inland waterway transport boards are not covered by the directive at all.

The government is a continuous and big buyer, and has the power to stipulate conditions which force the seller to introduce new technology, stimulate innovation and standardization, and encourage the use of new techniques conducive to efficiency, such as budgetary control, critical path analysis, value engineering and quality control. But no European government has learnt to use this power effectively. In Britain, 5 per cent of total output of all manufacturing and construction industries is bought by the central government and another $8\frac{1}{2}$ per cent by the rest of the public sector – local authorities and public corporations. But the Labour Government seem to have dropped their ambitious plans for deploying this immense buying power to accelerate technological progress.[14]

There is a strong case for mobilising the purchasing power of European governments and coordinating public sector purchases of high technology equipment for state transport, communications and energy agencies, and a strong case for an element of discrimination by enacting a 'Buy European' Act similar to the 'Buy American' Act under which European-made products would enjoy preference unless there was a price discrepancy of more than a certain amount. The difficulty is that there is no broad basis of agreement about political, and hence economic and strategic aims and needs on which to build a common system of procurement. The *Benelux Customs Union* (1947) agreement between Holland, Belgium and Luxembourg, when upgraded into an economic union in 1958, did stipulate that there was to be no discrimination in the procurement of goods and services by the central governments in favour of national products or national suppliers of one of the three member states, but no joint system of procurement was ever evolved. The *European Defence Community* included plans for the joint buying of military equipment, and the *Air Union* idea had as one of its aims the joint purchase of aircraft and parts for the national airlines of Europe. But this proposal fell down over this very issue. No agreement could be reached over procurement procedures and policy. Some wanted to follow a 'buy European' policy – which in effect meant a buy French policy, while others wanted to be free to apply commercial criteria in their buying. The experience of past attempts at the joint production and procurement of arms under NATO and WEU are no more encouraging.[15] As Jean Monnet once said, it is easy to integrate businessmen but almost impossible to integrate governments. A common purchasing policy by public authorities seems to subsume a degree of political identity and purpose which simply does not exist as yet between European countries.

Since the signing of the Rome Treaty there has been a rapid increase in company mergers as a defensive reaction against increased regional competition within the Common Market and mounting pressure from outside. Spurred by competition and prodded by governments, mergers are becoming increasingly popular, although amalgamations do not appear to have reached the same intensity inside the Common Market as in Britain where some 900 mergers occur each year. Mergers have been most prevalent in automobiles, shipbuilding, household appliances, photographic equipment, auto tyres and machinery, computers, aircraft and steel. The increasing size of companies in steel is encouraged by the ECSC's High Authority whenever this is likely to result in greater efficiency and economies of scale. Some important steel consolidations in recent months have been Dortmund-Hoerder-Hütenunion with Hoesch and with Hoogoverns, and Thyssen with Phoenix-Rheinruhr, who together now produce 25 per cent of Germany's steel output. In France, Usinor joined with Lorraine-Escaut to supply 30 per cent of the French steel market, and in Luxembourg ARBED and Hadir have joined to produce virtually all of that country's steel production. A major consolidation in chemicals has been that of Montecatini and Edison, the fourth and fifth largest Italian companies, who together supply 80 per cent of the Italian chemicals market. Nevertheless, industrial concentration measured on a European basis is still much lower than in the United States and even Japan. Montecatini-Edison only produce 15 per cent of the Common Market's supply of chemicals, and Thyssen-Phoenix 10 per cent of its steel.

European governments have been active in promoting national concentrations by exhortation and incentive. The 'monopoly bogey' which for so long has restricted the formation of larger units has been laid at last. The British Government has established the *Industrial Reorganization Corporation* (IRC) to facilitate desirable business concentration, including intra-European mergers. The French Government under the Fifth Plan (1966–70) aim to reduce the number of independent concerns by creating larger groups in aluminium, steel, machinery, electrical construction, aeronautics, motor manufacturing, electronics, pharmaceuticals and chemicals. The *Plan Calcul*, within the framework of the Plan, is designed to rationalize French computer interests. The two remaining independent electronics firms, the CAI computer division of CITEC, and SEA, a subsidiary of Schneider, have been merged, and Cie des Compteurs and Thomson-Houston/Hotchkiss-Brandt (another recent merger), both major producers of electrical appliances, have created a joint subsidiary to build computers.

But while rationalization has been proceeding apace at the national level, and although there have been plenty of international joint undertakings and other forms of cross-frontier links, there have been precious few outright inter-country amalgamations in Europe to date. Hard facts are scarce but Dutch merger statistics give an indication of the general pattern. Between 1958 and 1965 there were 258 mergers in all, of which 175 were with other Dutch companies and 83 with foreign companies. Of the foreign mergers, 42 were with North American companies and only 8 with firms of EEC countries.[16] Since the inception of the Community there has been only one notable transnational merger – the Agfa-Gevaert team-up – which was dictated by reasons of research. The giant American company, Kodak, spent almost as much on research as Gevaert's total sales.

The EEC Commission recognizes that size offers advantages in the diversification and stabilization of risks, in better marketing and in the reduction of distribution costs, and in high volume, low-cost methods of producton. But except for the small number of industries where large-scale plants are a technical and economic necessity, the Commission considers that the main arguments in favour of big companies are concerned with finance and research, and that in both cases international mergers offer better prospects than national mergers.[17]

Differences in company and fiscal legislation in Community countries, and psychological factors, have proved an important obstacle to the formation of European-wide combinations despite intensified competition. In order to encourage the growth of European-scale companies, and to help firms to adapt themselves to the larger market in Europe and face the increasing competition from outside, the Commission have drawn up a five-point plan: to remove tax barriers to the expansion of Community companies, to free all restrictions on intra-European trade, to establish a Community patent system, to strengthen medium-sized and smaller firms, and to establish a European system of company law. On the last point there is a proposal in the pipeline for a European form of company which would not be subject to the legal systems of the several member states and would not have the nationality of any specific state, but would operate within the Common Market under Community law. This would be established by means of a convention appended to the Rome Treaty.[18] The Commission's approach to the question of larger units however, is one of strict neutrality in that it seeks only to remove artificial hindrances to mergers and has no policy for deliberately fostering industrial concentration. It believes that companies should be responsible for choosing their own optimum size according to the nature of their products, the scale and structure of the market, marketing techniques, and the needs of research and finance. In view of the psychological impediments to transnational mergers it might be wondered whether the removal of artificial barriers alone will be enough to encourage European companies to gear themselves to a scale sufficient to meet external competition, and whether it may not prove necessary to create a European organization comparable to the Industrial Reorganization Corporation to effect amalgamations.

While favouring larger units the EEC Commission has dededeclared itself opposed to oligopolies and monopolies which destroy competition.[19] International conditions may nevertheless demand that some companies grow to a more than optimum size for the European market in order to compete on level terms with American companies. A recent study on competition and concentration in Europe endorses this view: '... the heart of the dilemma between concentration and competition arises from the fact that *in some cases* greater size, with a consequent emergence of monopoly and oligopoly, may be indispensable if economies of scale are to be fully reaped or R & D thresholds surmounted. Indeed, the likelihood that such a situation will emerge is considerably greater in the EEC than in the United States. This arises from the fact that if, in order to compete with US industry, European enterprises have to emulate their US counterparts in the matter of size, then, by virtue of the fact that the US market is more than twice the size of that of the Community, it follows that the Community market will support fewer optimum-sized enterprises than that of the United States. The degree of concentration in the Community must therefore be greater than that in the United States. As a result, to a greater extent in Europe than in the United States, market power and oligopolistic market behaviour may be an inevitable concomitant of optimum size.'[20] It seems probable therefore that sections of the Common

Market in the future must be dominated by a small number of large firms – bigness with fewness.

*

While research is a major activity of EURATOM and an important aspect of the work of ECSC, it is mentioned only once in the Rome Treaty, namely in Article 41, which states that provision may be made for the coordination of research in the agricultural sector. There are no chapters on a common science policy although indirect scope for such a policy could be interpreted from some of the more general provisions of the Treaty which call for the closest cooperation in economic policy. The fusion of the executives of the three communities may help to facilitate the coordination of activities in research matters, but this fusion does not alter the dispositions of the Treaties. This is a serious omission, and, as is now recognized, it will have to be amended when the three Treaties themselves come to be merged. While awaiting a wider mandate the single Commission is nevertheless free to take action under what powers it has, and is of course free to proceed and strengthen the industrial/market base of the Six which in some ways is the most important ingredient of a 'technological community'. Some preparatory steps towards a Community research policy have already been taken.

In a recommendation to the EEC Council in July 1963, relative to a medium-term economic policy, the Commission emphasized for the first time the necessity of extending Community cooperation to the scientific research and technological fields. As a result of this recommendation, a Working Party on science and technology was set up in March 1965 within the Committee on Medium-Term Economic Policy. It has the general task of studying the problems involved in the elaboration of a coordinated or common policy, and of proposing measures for the inauguration of such a policy with due regard to the possibilities of cooperation with third countries. In particular, it is to draw up a balance sheet of current research activities in member countries, compare the organization, structure, aims and methods of existing research programmes, and make an inventory of the sectors in which applied research seemed clearly inadequate. The first full report of the Working Party is expected in the autumn of 1967, but in the meantime they have submitted an interim report to the Committee on Medium-Term Economic Policy which allowed certain guide lines for scientific and technological research to be included in the Preliminary Draft of the Community's first medium-term programme. The Working Party particularly stressed the need for better information and as a response to this request the EEC Commission have commissioned a study on scientific research in the electronics industry.[21]

At the instance of EURATOM, and pending the merger of the executives, an Inter-Executive Committee on scientific and technological research was set up in October 1965 to coordinate the approach of the three executives in the research field and lay down, in the light of their experience, the principles and guide lines of a common research policy. The EURATOM Commission regarded its experience in the nuclear field as the starting point for a broader scientific policy, and pointed out that its own research establishments could easily diversify into other fields of research, indeed, they had already done so in areas peripheral to nuclear activity. In this they had the support of the Liberal Group in the European Parliament.[22] But the idea was resisted by the EEC Commission on the grounds that a science policy could not be divorced from economic and industrial policy, and that therefore any future action must be undertaken by those responsible for economic policy – namely themselves.

Meanwhile, in March 1965 the French Government had submitted a memorandum to the EEC Council outlining its thinking on a Community scientific research and industrial policy. The Rome Treaty's requirement for smooth development of economic activity and continuous, balanced growth implied a joint effort in this sphere. If the Community wished to acquire everything needed for sustained economic growth it would have to mount an intensified, and if possible a coordinated, science

M

and technical research drive – the basic aim being to improve the competitive ability of Community states – particularly in those sectors where scientific advance was the most rapid, by utilizing the intellectual resources of each member state logically and on a scale commensurate with its ambition. This being so the French Government wished to see the Community begin two series of studies. The first to compare current civil research plans in the six states, the aim being to prevent future duplication and perhaps to allocate specific tasks between the member states research institutes, and to bring out the weak points of existing plans in the public and private sectors. The second area of the inquiry to identify the vulnerable sectors of industry in the Six, that is to say the sectors in which the amount of applied research was clearly inadequate by comparison with that being done in other countries or those advanced sectors whose dynamism was closely and directly dependent on the progress of research. The French Government was further of the opinion that a liberal attitude with regard to third countries implied that member states should undertake an investment policy designed to enable the industry of the Community to remain competitive, particularly *vis-à-vis* the industries of major countries which received considerable aid from the state. These inquiries might subsequently serve as a basis for the definition of a real common research policy.[23]

The European Parliament was also active in calling for a policy in science and technology, and goading the Commission into action. A useful study on the question was prepared by the Parliament's Commission for Research and Culture.[24] Despite the limitations of the Rome Treaty a science policy is therefore in the process of elaboration. The clearest indication of the Commission's thinking on the subject is contained in the speech of M. Marjolin in a debate of the European Parliament in October 1966. 'Certainly there is more and more talk today about scientific research and its importance, but it is doubtful whether public opinion has really appreciated the part played by science in our society.' The capacity for invention, and its corollary the capacity to exploit invention, now play a part similar to the possession of mineral deposits and sources of energy in the past. 'To be in the front rank of nations, it is not enough now to possess the equipment for mass production, you have to be able to remould your products and techniques at a pace which there is every reason to believe will grow in the future. Scientific and technological research has thus become an essential aspect of economic policy.'

The Commission considered that the lag in research was one of the main weaknesses in the Community, '... it was burdening the economic prospects of the Community with a mortgage which would fall due in a few years' time'. M. Marjolin suggested certain courses of action that might be taken to stimulate research: raise the level of higher education and make liberal grants in aid of research to universities and similar institutions; increase the public contribution to applied research and development either for work executed directly by the state, or for projects carried out by cooperation between the government and private industry; remove all obstacles to the formation of firms of optimum size which do not mean monopolies or near monopolies; pursue an economic policy which would enable firms to formulate R & D work on a much bigger scale than at present. Efforts should also be made in taxation and patent law. It was not enough, however, just to spend more money; money must be spent intelligently.

With regard to the part to be played by the Community, M. Marjolin suggested action along the following lines: a broader scope for Community activities when the Treaties were amalgamated, but in the meanwhile it was necessary to proceed pragmatically. Support should be given to a small number of highly important projects in which the member states might take part in varying degrees. Possibly non-member states, in particular Great Britain, should be associated with some of these projects. The deficiencies in national programmes should be identified, and coordinated or concerted actions planned. The climate for research could be improved by agreeing on a European patent law, the creation of a European-type company, and the elimination of other obstacles which prevent

European firms from attaining optimum size. In certain sectors orders from Community governments might be pooled and passed on to industry in relation to the research it had carried out. The development of public aid should also be encouraged provided this did not distort competition. The widest possible dissemination should be given to scientific knowledge; there was need for clearing houses for scientific information on a European or an even wider scale. The freedom of movement of research workers and cooperation between universities should be encouraged.[25]

In March 1967, the three Executives submitted a Joint-Memorandum to the Council for consideration. The Memorandum stresses the link between research and economic growth and examines the reasons for the greater technological strength of the USA. The Executives stress that the removal of customs duties between the Six is not enough to provide a sufficient stimulus to progress in Europe. Further measures implementing the Rome Treaty are necessary before industry and business in the Community will be compelled to undertake the organizational changes necessary in a continental-size market. Insufficient market incentives are one of the main causes of the deteriorating situation. The Memorandum points out that a large part of American industry's strength derives from the action of the public authorities, not only in financing R & D but also in purchasing the end-products. European companies had not benefited to anything like the same extent from public policy. The Executives also suggested that some foreign-owned companies had reduced or eliminated the research capacity of European companies which had passed under their control.

The Executives recommend that Europe should concentrate on building up her strength in certain fields but an essential precondition of this is the achievement of economic unity including a European patent law, the free movement of capital, the elimination of technical barriers to trade through standardization, non-discrimination in granting contracts for public works, a European company law and fiscal measures to facilitate mergers on a continental scale.

Studies should be made of how member governments could consolidate their public contracts, especially in the advanced technologies. This would offer key industries a wider and more guaranteed market. Studies should also be made on the present form and effectiveness of state aids – R & D contracts and insurance against technological risks, and other aspects of national programmes, with the aim of avoiding distortions, dispersal of effort and the pursuit of contradictory aims. Ways must also be found of more effective cooperation; after establishing the cause of present difficulties in some cooperative ventures, a coordinated or common programme could be put on foot. To halt the brain-drain a study should be conducted of educational methods and facilities, on means of improving the professional situation of researchers, on the state financing of research facilities in universities, on cooperation between research centres and European centres of information. And finally, the Memorandum urges a study of how the Community can undertake scientific cooperation with other European countries and with the USA, including the exchange of information, exchanges visits by research workers, and participation in joint projects and programmes.[26]

All this is just talk and it remains to be seen what will be followed up and what action taken. Many people feel that the Community context is inadequate for the balance to be redressed. On the strength of this the Italian Foreign Minister, Signor Fanfani, has put forward a transatlantic plan for the 'technological rehabilitation' of Europe for which NATO is suggested as the framework. A ten year 'Marshall Aid' type programme of trans-Atlantic cooperation is envisaged in fields where joint action is urgently needed – aerospace, commercial, scientific and industrial satellites, nuclear research, desalination, computers, air purification and the training of scientists and technologists. The plan aims to prevent duplication of effort both between European countries and between Europe and the United States. For Europe to catch up a comparable effort would be necessary to that of the United States, but to derive benefit from this enhanced effort European industries must reach full continental scale. The idea was discussed by the NATO Ministers in December 1966.

The Americans have rather resented the idea that it is up to the United States to help close the gap. In their view the gap is primarily a management and education gap which it is up to Europeans themselves to close.[27] However, in response to the clamour President Johnson recently appointed a committee of experts to consider what the United States might do. Yet it is hard to see how the US could provide effective help. As the research director of Philips' ironically remarked: 'If America really wants to do something, let it start introducing different currencies in all the fifty states and impose serious boundaries between them. If this experiment were tried, ten or fifteen years from now we might well bridge the gap.' The real prescription of course lies in European hands – tear down the old nationalistic economic walls that divide the markets, restricting competition and protecting inefficiency, and create an industrial environment favourable to technological progress.

At the OECD Ministers meeting in Paris in January 1966, it was suggested that one area of international cooperation where some real progress was feasible without waiting for political and economic agreement in Europe was fundamental research. A community of European science, 'a common market of ideas and scholarship', could be established by planning university research in concert and setting up a network of specialized European Centres of Advanced Study and Research based on existing institutions in individual countries. By virtue of this status these centres would be given selective encouragement and support in the interests of Europe as a whole. Additionally, there could be a Council of the European Centres of Advanced Study and Research to coordinate the work of the centres and encourage the exchange of research workers on an effective scale; this could be the nucleus of a European Science Council.[28] The idea has the support of Lord Flory, past President of the Royal Society: '... Much more, I believe, could be done to forward discovery by making use of selected environments throughout the world into which concerted effort could be put. By this I mean that instead of spreading our national resources too thinly between too many institutions we should concentrate on "centres of excellence", and from firm national bases international "centres of excellence" could be formed. We might then hear less of the brain-drain, and if some of our best people did go to work in other countries, their going would be balanced at least partially by a reverse flow.'[29]

The schemes for a European Scientific and Technological Community are altogether more ambitious. This Community would have its own supra-national institutions – a Scientific and Technological Authority headed by a European Minister of Technology, advised by a Council for Science and Technology. The Authority would have the mandate to formulate a science policy for Europe and would seek to prevent duplication by rationalizing R & D efforts. Priorities would be selected after weighing up the economic, social, political and scientific benefits of projects and programmes. Among other things the Community would establish a patents pool and centres of excellence – key European centres in particular fields of study open to all European scientists. A common purchasing policy by public buyers would be worked out, and the Authority would have the power to award development contracts to industry on a European basis.[30]

The idea of a Technological Community has found its strongest support in Britain where all the main political parties have backed it. Advocates have seen it as a means of associating Britain with the Common Market prior to full membership,[31] and as a way of breaking the present log-jam and generating pressures towards the achievement of full European unity. It is argued that here is an area where the Six are weak and Britain comparatively strong. Britain has something to offer. According to the most detailed of these proposals the new Community would embrace all EEC and EFTA countries and provide for the integration of the technologically advanced industries, beginning with the abolition, at one blow, of all tariffs on high technology products. Joint R & D programmes would be carried out under the control of a powerful supra-national secretariat with its own funds for research and for procurement. The proposals for a European patent and European company would be put on an all-European basis. The idea, however, is considered inseparable from the other communities, the aim being from the outset to merge it with the EEC. The idea in fact is essentially a political initiative, for the new Community 'will have served its purpose if it confers momentum on the discussions between Britain and the Six, if it dramatizes the benefits which British membership will bring and if it enables the EEC to widen its purpose to embrace the vast possibilities of science-based industries.'[32]

This idea the Prime Minister made his own. At the Lord Mayor's Banquet in November 1966 he said, 'We have much to contribute to the European Community including change. It was never ordained from on high that there should be only three such European communities ... I should like to see ... a drive to create a new technological community to pool with Europe the enormous technological inventiveness of Britain and other European countries, to enable Europe on a competitive basis to become more self-reliant and neither dependent on imports nor dominated from outside, but basing itself on the creation of competitive, indigenous European industries ... I can think of nothing that would make a greater reality of the whole European concept. And in this field of technological cooperation no one has more to contribute than Britain.'

The Prime Minister was quite right to lay emphasis on Britain's technological prowess. She has more Nobel Prizes to her credit than any other European state and her percentage of scientists and technologists per head is only surpassed in America and Russia. She is the only western country outside of America with a favourable balance of patent-payments account and, after Germany, she is Europe's second largest exporter of inventions (as measured by the number of patents). Britain again is the only country in Europe with a sizeable stock of natural uranium and the only one capable of producing highly enriched uranium, and with the know-how to fabricate H-bombs. She is very strong in nuclear technology generally and certainly has a commanding lead over her neighbours in this field. The volume of her exports of radioisotopes is the largest in the world. She is the only European country with a computer industry worth talking about, with a possible world lead in process control. She has more qualified computer personnel, programmers and systems analysts, and is Europe's chief exporter of electronic goods. She is the only one possessing an inertial guidance system and the only one with the capacity to compete with America and Russia in radio-astronomy. She possesses the most powerful particle accelerator (outside of CERN) and has a world lead in desalination technology, having installed two-thirds of the world's present capacity. She is the only real partner France has got in aerospace. Rolls-Royce have equipped half the world's airliners with jet engines, and Decca half the world's merchant marine with radar. In the past she pioneered radio, television, radar and the jet engine, and at the present the hovercraft, VTOL flight and hydrostatic extrusion – to name but a few of her credentials.

These facts have not gone unnoticed in Europe, in France in particular. Any plans to strengthen Europe scientifically and technologically must necessarily depend on the experience and support of Britain. The European Parliament indeed, when discussing the proposals to enlarge the competence of EURATOM in science and technology, actively considered the possibility of inviting Britain to join the Atomic Energy Community, '... so as to take part from the beginning in the common policy on science and technology, establishing thereby, amongst other things, a useful stage towards her final integration in the construction of a United Europe.'[33]

But while Mr Wilson was undoubtedly right to stress Britain's strength in technology it was unfortunate that he should have proposed a fourth Community, additional to the existing three, for as the Leader of the Opposition pointed out in the House of Commons, 'The Prime Minister mentioned the creation of a Technological Community. I fully accept that we have much to contribute technologically, but... we must

recognize that we are now in the state in which the Six are prepared to fuse the Executives of the existing three communities.
It is, therefore, unlikely that they will wish to create a fourth
community of the kind that the Prime Minister has put
forward.'[34]

In his speech at the Churchill Banquet on November 30 the
Prime Minister seems to have come nearer the point of view
that any technological initiative could only be taken within
the Common Market: 'American technological dominance in
so many parts of the world derives from the original opportunities presented by her own wide, dynamic, open market:
it derives, too, from the fact that her industries are sufficiently
developed and massive, sufficiently free from undue fragmenta-
tion, to enable her to reap the advantages of large-scale production which modern technology demands, and will in increasing
measure demand. So it must be for us.... This is why in our
readiness to join the European Community we have said that
we regard that Community not as static... but as dynamic.
We have much to bring to Europe including change. We see
Europe as a technological community capable of the same
dynamic growth as America has achieved, given the right
framework in which to operate.'

At this point the idea of a separate, fourth community seems
to have been dropped although the Prime Minister continued
to underline the technological benefits Britain could bring to
the Community in his tour of the six capitals. The technology
gap had become a sensitive issue with anti-American overtones. Mr Kosygin, in his visit to Paris, had already fanned the
flames of resentment. Mr Wilson now added his fuel by warning the Council of Europe, in January 1957, of '... an industrial helotry under which we in Europe produce only the conventional apparatus of a modern economy, while becoming
increasingly dependent on American business for the sophisticated apparatus which will call the industrial tune in the '70's
and '80's.' But by the close of his talks in Brussels it was clear
that Mr Wilson had wholly come round to the view that any
plans for closing the technology gap could only be effective

within the framework of an enlarged and reinforced Common Market. When asked to expand on his ideas of a Technological Community in the House of Commons in April 1967, he replied: 'The three communities which now exist are to be merged. This proposal should really be read in terms of the techno-logical component in the new merged and enlarged Com-munity. I do not think that the cooperation required in Europe in technology necessarily requires anything significant in the way of supra-national superstructure. What I am strongly con-vinced about is that the degree of technological cooperation which is possible can only flourish if it is within a single inter-national trading market. . . . It is certainly true that we have a great deal to contribute to Europe. . . . This could only func-tion adequately, not on the basis of an exchange of learned papers across the present division of Europe, but within a single trading Community.'

An enlarged single trading Community is of course the ideal solution. But if in fact it should prove impossible at present to end the division in Europe, it might still be desirable to re-vert to the old sector approach to integration in an area which is 'inherently expansive' and set up a 'fourth' Technological Community. There is no reason why patents, company law and technical standards should not be put on an all-European basis, and no reason why the OECD proposal for a 'common market of ideas and scholarship' should not be implemented. A return to the sector approach was advocated by the distin-guished French engineer, Louis Armand, during the deadlock in the Community in 1965 under the caption 'Federalism à la carte'. This would entail a number of steps to develop Euro-pean infrastructures outside of the formal framework of the EEC. New ways of progress without abandoning those al-ready available. 'European unification has not kept up with the quickening pace of events. The result is that Europe more and more lets America take the lead in technical inventions . . . in so doing she is being taken in tow by America. This situation will become more serious if Europeans do not make a con-certed effort to create forms and institutions, in both the intellectual and industrial spheres, modelled on those which enable the United States to enjoy a higher standard of living and, what is more, to make better preparations for the future; in other words, a strong impetus towards Europeanization is needed to offset an imbalance which is likely to become irreversible. . . .

'More than ever it is necessary to forge ahead and if . . . the centre of the European front – the Community – is marking time, the flanks must be pushed forward: steps must be taken which, despite the political climate, will contribute to the development of European infrastructures in other vital fields.' In many areas the framework of the Six is inadequate. Federalism *à la carte* is intended to enable various European countries to associate in accordance with their desires and interests so as to create durable links in limited fields. 'It is not intended to oppose the closer union already achieved by the six countries . . . still less to replace it . . . the object of this kind of federalism would be to supplement and amplify the Treaties by agreements governing specific sectors which are vital to Europe's future but which were not built into the Rome Treaty.'[35]

THE POLITICAL IMPERATIVE

With all these proposals in the wind one is inevitably left wondering what will become of them all and whether any real progress will be made. Have our leaders really appreciated the importance of science in modern society and have they drawn all the inferences? A science policy after all is not only concerned with scientific priorities, but also with political and economic goals. So long as Europe remains politically divided it is difficult to see what progress can be made in evolving a science policy. A science policy is only meaningful in the context of the broader political and social objectives that science serves and can only be effectively implemented by bodies responsible for achieving such objectives. In analysing the factors which enabled the United States to outstrip Europe, the Joint-Memorandum of the three executives quoted earlier notes that the decisive factor is the existence of a single political authority, able to allocate substantial resources and to mobilize the means necessary for attaining technological policy aims. But in Europe there is no single political authority or international organization to formulate a consistent and comprehensive international science policy. That is the rub. The policies of the various international organizations are derivative, that is to say they emerge out of the individual policies of the cooperating nations. 'The spectrum within which any political group can formulate a policy for scientific advance ... is determined by its over-all objectives. Within a nation, political objectives cover the full range of national aspiration, and their form and interrelations are subject to decisions of nationwide authority. . . . There is no international analogue to this situation. No international organization has an over-all mandate or single decision-making authority covering all aspects of international cooperation. None is therefore in a position to formulate or implement an effective policy covering all international scientific activities. To the extent that the political objectives of each are particular and restricted, the science-policy function of each must also be particular and restricted by its relevance to those objectives.'[36]

International organizations are really nothing more than the sum of their component parts. They are not a political entity in their own right, establishing, pursuing and enforcing collective policy. According to one authority: 'International organizations are nothing more than the instruments of policies of individual governments, the means of diplomacy of a number of disparate and sovereign states. When inter-governmental organizations are set up, this implies nothing more than that between the states a limited agreement has been reached upon an institutional form for multilateral conduct of state activity in certain fields. The organization becomes important for the pursuance of national policies precisely to the extent that such a multilateral coordination is the real and continuous aim of national governments.'[37]

So long as it remains true that agreements are only instruments of national policy, 'sets of mutual promises of coordination and synchronization of national policy activities initiated by the states themselves', the possibility of any real progress must be considered remote. The former French Minister of Science, Gaston Palewski, faced the issue squarely when addressing a joint OECD/Council of Europe meeting in 1965: 'Cooperation in science is affected by the still embryonic and in some respects rudimentary character of the international community. It is a good thing certainly that the States have, to this extent, recognized the need for international cooperation in so many fields. . . .

'I think, however, that it would be idle to hope to achieve anything satisfactory so long as States do not display a common political will. . . . Since science has become an instrument of policy, it will no longer be possible "to do our science together" unless we do our politics together. This affirmation may seem too categorical but I think that it is true in view of the decisive role played by science in the world today. Let us not be afraid to say so. A group of States can only pool the totality of their scientific resources if they have agreed on the same internal, economic, social and external policy.

'As we are still a long way from this, the different attempts at scientific cooperation naturally remain of a partial nature. The States may easily agree on limited subjects . . . but they cannot agree on an overall scientific policy.

'Another obstacle to a relatively extensive cooperation is the unequal development of the different countries. It is natural that countries which are already well advanced in scientific research should have difficulties in passing on their knowledge to less advanced countries. This is true of military research but equally true of research with purely civilian applications. Hence the obstacles in the way of an overall scientific cooperation between Europe and the United States.

'There is a corollary to this, namely that two countries must be of equal or comparable strength in a given field for them to agree to cooperate. . . . Well, you may say, these difficulties are not a reason for resigning ourselves to the luxuriant though limited anarchy of today. We must, of course, endeavour to improve this cooperation. But we shall only succeed in doing so if we face the realities of the situation. It is only by doing so that we can try to modify these realities.'[38]

This is the reality, it is true; and it must be modified. If Europe wishes to remain a technological 'third force' in the world, capable of competing against, or partnering, others on a basis of equality, some progress towards political unity is absolutely indispensable. Cooperation is not enough.

Chapter VI

The Maturing Crisis

Technology has its own geographical rules and dimensions, and to comply with its needs and requirements nations are obliged to work together. But any nation which wishes to profit from the full support of technology must also be prepared to adjust the scale of its political and economic organization to the level of techniques. Realizing that the world has become very small, and calls for standards of size different from those applied in the European patchwork of yesterday, and appreciating that their economies can exploit the opportunities offered by modern techniques and compete with today's giants only if they are conceived on a large scale, the six members of the Common Market have already made a beginning. And now it seems that Britain is willing, if others are willing, to make a beginning also. But it will still be said that this is all very interesting but thanks just the same we prefer to stay as we are. We, ourselves, alone. 'Our own little, snug little, tight little Island.' And why not? Of course, for a country as dependent on external operations for its livelihood as Britain, both to renounce the opportunity of creating conditions more favourable to progress, and the opportunity of retaining some political power to influence the conditions in which it must operate, can hardly be considered the most astute or prudent policy to pursue. It must even be considered rather daring. Nevertheless, if political independence and sovereignty (whatever that that may mean in this situation) is really valued more highly than prosperity, progress, security and power, then 'we, ourselves, alone' would be a perfectly practicable course of action to take. After all, a great deal can be gained from straight-forward international cooperation of the old style without re-course to political integration. The idea that we must, at all costs, get into Europe or go under is pure hysteria. If we chose, we could stand alone as a small country amongst large.

OUR FINITE GLOBE

However, the technological case for a United Europe does not end there. There is a further problem of technological pro-gress which tilts the balance more clearly in favour of an inter-national experiment of this kind. It has nothing to do with the power and wealth of individual or groups of nations. It arises from our growing influence over natural processes and to the reaching of certain critical relationships. This will require global planning and control because the effects we are beginning to produce are of the same order of magnitude as the globe itself. They affect the earth as an entity.

The American mathematician, the late Dr John von Neumann, once called this the 'maturing crisis of technology'. This is what he had to say; 'The great globe itself is in a rapidly maturing crisis – a crisis attributable to the fact that the en-vironment in which technological progress must occur has be-come both undersized and underorganized ...

'In the first half of this century the accelerating Industrial Revolution encountered an absolute limitation – not on tech-nological progress as such, but on an essential safety factor. This safety factor ... was essentially a matter of geographical and political *lebensraum* : an ever broader scope for techno-logical activities, combined with ever broader political integra-tion in the world. Within this expanding framework it was possible to accommodate the major tensions created by techno-logical progress.

'Now this safety mechanism is being sharply inhibited: liter-ally and figuratively, we are running out of room. At long last, we begin to feel the effects of the finite, actual size of the earth in a critical way.

N

'Thus the crisis does not arise from accidental events or human errors. It is inherent in technology's relation to geography on the one hand and to political organization on the other.'[1]

Nuclear weapons are the most obvious example of large scale technology with world-wide implications and repercussions – where we feel the finite size of the earth in a critical way. Initially a nuclear war would cause a massive destruction of people, industry, resources and agriculture in the belligerent countries. But due to the fall-out hazards and the build up of radio-active contamination, it would also have immediate and long-term consequences for human health and life in the world at large. Some scientists fear that these dangers would be amplified by the complex feedbacks in our environment, and that an ecological imbalance would be induced. Huge, uncontrollable and irreversible effects might be triggered by the massive disturbance of natural processes. The destruction of vegetation would result in the erosion and sterilization of the land. Vast quantities of dust might be injected into the stratosphere, shading the earth from sunlight and cutting down the amount of solar heat received at the earth's surface, setting off catastrophic climatic changes.

All this is conjecture. The truth is that we can only guess at the effects of a full-scale nuclear war. But some of the biological consequences of nuclear tests have already been visited upon us through the contamination of the earth's air masses, plants, animals and humans. An awareness of these dangers, and their unpredictable effects, was one of the reasons which persuaded some of the nuclear powers to sign the Test-Ban Treaty.

When the United States proposed to detonate a nuclear device in the Van Allen radiation belts which girdle the earth – 'Project Starfish' – with the aim of measuring the effect of high-altitude nuclear explosions on military communications, there were protests from scientists throughout the world, pointing to the danger of producing long-lasting changes in these belts with unforseeable and unalterable consequences. Sir Bernard Lovell was one of those who protested. Writing on the subject in the *Sunday Times*, he argued; 'We are now immersed in a period of great interest in solar and interplanetary physics, equipped with the powerful tools of space research to put various ideas to the test of experimental investigation. This situation is distinguished from many other similar ones in contemporary research by the vital fact that the laboratory in which the experiments must be made belongs not to one scientist or one nation but to all humanity . . . there is at the moment little evidence of the moral and legal controls which must be enforced if man's continued life on earth is not to be jeopardized by the accidental or intentional results of space research.'[2]

Nuclear weapons are the most serious of the global technologies because they, and their problems, are already with us. But in some respect they are the least of our worries and are unlikely to prove the most dangerous and intractable of our involvements. Nuclear weapons, after all, do not have to be used. It is a question of human choice. With patience and intelligence their use may yet be avoided. But in the case of other technological operations of world-wide significance there will be no choice over their use.

The human race has been learning to control the microclimate since time immemorial. Heating and ventilation systems, diet and exercise, irrigation, land drainage and soil conservation, are all techniques which in aggregate are sufficient, within extremes, to counter-balance the macro-climate – permitting the areas of the globe suitable for human habitation and activity to be constantly expanded. But we now have the knowledge to modify the macro-climate itself, and instead of adjusting ourselves to the environmental conditions of the earth we have the means to reverse the order of adaptation and make the earth conform to *our* existence.

Perhaps this seems somewhat far-fetched. The fact of the matter is, however, that more than forty power companies in the USA are already engaged in weather modification programmes, and, according to the Director of the National Centre for Atmosphere Research, the United States will be in a position to attempt major changes in its weather within ten years. Recently, in a report to the President on the subject, the National Academy of Science suggested that new computer techniques and meteorological satellites for monitoring now made possible a rational and systematic exploration of modification techniques, and urged that thirty million dollars be put aside for an initial programme.[3]

Australia, America and Israel have employed rain-making techniques to quench forest fires and improve agricultural land. Rain is induced by sowing cumulus clouds with silver iodide or solid carbon dioxide. The effects are local and temporary. Climate modification proposals, in contrast, would be long-term and have regional or world-wide scope. If our ability to modify the weather depended on a contest of strength with nature there would be little prospect of success. The energy of the winds circulating the earth is equal to between ten thousand and a hundred thousand simultaneous metagon explosions. Even a good thunderstorm is comparable in power to an H-bomb and there are up to two thousand thunderstorms in progress around the world at any one time. Ideas for weather modification work on the principle that quite small forces can be used to trigger very large ones. All weather phenomena are ultimately controlled by the solar energy that falls on the earth, sea and atmosphere, and this seems to be subject to delicate influences. By altering the thermal properties of limited ground areas it is thought possible to generate convection currents and cause precipitation over deserts. Russian scientists are of the opinion that the Arctic icecap absorbs heat from the surrounding landmass and reflects sunlight back into space. They suggest that by darkening the surface of the ice the solar energy would be absorbed rather than reflected. A reduction in the area of the ice would follow, bringing a radical improvement in the climate of these northern extremes.

The difficulty is that interventions of this kind and on this dimension would have world-wide repercussions, with effects impossible to gauge beforehand. Because of their scale, the permissible margin of error is very small. The dangers attendant on inducing changes on such a magnitude with imperfect understanding of the consequences cannot be overemphasized. The average annual temperature of the earth during the last Ice Age, ten thousand years ago, was only 15 degrees colder than today's temperature. In the present underorganized state of the world who is to control techniques of this scale? And just how sovereign do nations think they are going to be in this situation? To quote von Neumann again; '... there is in most of these developments a trend towards affecting the globe as a whole, or, to be more exact, toward producing effects that can be projected from any one to any other point on the earth. There is an intrinsic conflict with geography – and institutions based thereon – as understood today. Of course, any technology interacts with geography, and each imposes its own geographical rules and modalities. The technology that is now developing and that will dominate the next decades seems to be in total conflict with traditional and, in the main, momentarily still valid geographical and political units and concepts. This is the maturing crisis of technology.'

The notion that a solution to this crisis can be found by postponing the use of technologies of this magnitude until the world grows up, closes the institutional lag, and organizes itself on a scale commensurate with the tools it now has at its disposal, can be dismissed out of hand. Apart from the inherent usefulness of being able to manipulate the weather, we shall be required to exploit these technologies to balance and control processes which have unintentionally been set in train in our developing world.

During the past century at least 400 000 million tons of carbon dioxide have been artificially introduced into our atmosphere by the burning of fossil fuels – increasing the concentration of carbon dioxide in the air by 14 per cent. America dumps 85 million tons of 'aerial garbage' into her atmosphere each year from vehicle exhausts alone (carbon monoxide, sulphur dioxide, oxides of nitrogen and hydrocarbons). A further 22 million tons is accounted for by industry, 15 million by electrical power generation, 8 million by space heating and 3

N*

million by refuse burning. There seems little doubt that this build up of contamination is unintentionally altering the temperature regime which controls the wind current circulation. And certainly it has been shown that car exhaust has an important influence on local climate.[4]

Carbon dioxide in the atmosphere creates a sort of 'greenhouse' effect, allowing sunlight to reach the earth's surface but limiting the re-radiation of heat into space. As a consequence some scientists believe that the heat-balance of the earth is gradually being disturbed, and that if the present rate of aerial contamination continues the mean annual temperature all over the world may increase by 3.6 degrees in the next 40–50 years. That would be sufficient to begin melting the Greenland and Antarctic icecap. Preposterous? Not according to the President's Science Advisory Committee.[5] They claim that the ice may take anything from 400–4 000 years to melt, raising the sea level by 400 ft and drowning most of the world's major cities and much of its best inhabitable land. The Committee estimate that if a 1 000 years is required to melt all the ice, then, as from the end of this century, the sea level would be rising at the rate of 40 ft every hundred years.

Fumes and smoke are not the only pollutants damaging the quality of the air and accelerating the natural phenomena of climate cycles. Afforestation, deforestation, atmospheric explosions, irrigation and other alterations to the landscape, city buildings, flying aircraft, rocket exhausts, and the dispersal of 'exotic' materials in space research, like sodium, are all believed in some degree to be upsetting the climatic stability of our planet. In the case of space research it seems that actual rocket debris is unlikely to have much effect since the amount is infinitesimal compared with the ten thousand tons of meteorite material falling on the earth each day. The deleterious effects of space research on our climate is more likely to be caused by the exhaust of rockets since gases are important in marking the balance between incoming and outcoming radiation.[6]

The atmosphere is not the only part of our environment

subject to these invasions. Radio-active particles, detergents, pesticides, weed-killers, and industrial wastes are combining with the elements of the soil and entering into the biochemical processes of plants, micro-organisms, insects, animals and humans.[7] Since lead was added to petrol in 1923 to reduce 'knock' in engines there has been a steady build-up of this poison throughout the world. It has even been found in the snow and ice of Greenland. Some biologists fear that the ecological equilibrium of the world is being disrupted by the scale of these interventions. The tolerances within which we live are very narrow. Our life sustaining environment forms a vast community in which animals, plants, micro-organisms, soil and water are all tied together in an elaborate network of mutual relationships. Due to the interaction of the parts, the disturbance of one magnifies the repercussions and sets up a chain-reaction. One biologist, who has made a study of these problems, concluded; '... we have come to a turning point in the human habitation of the earth. The environment is a complex, subtly balanced system, and it is this integrated whole which receives the impact of all the separate insults inflicted by pollutants. Never before in the history of this planet has its thin life-supporting surface been subjected to such diverse, novel and potent agents. I believe that the cumulative effects of these pollutants, their interactions and amplification, can be fatal to the complex fabric of the biosphere. And, because man is, after all, a dependent part of this system, I believe that continued pollution of the earth, if unchecked, will eventually destroy the fitness of this planet as a place for human life.'[8]

Man has always influenced his surroundings, deliberately and unintentionally. In the past the desiccation of the climate by deforestation had the effect of destroying the prosperity of states and denuding whole regions of organized life. Witness the areas of North Africa and the Middle East which were once the great wheat lands of the Roman Empire. But these disruptions were usually restricted in time or space. Today our interventions are neither local nor brief. Never before have we done such grievous, irreversible violence to the delicate balance of natural processes.

The 'population explosion' is the most disturbing example of the increasing instability between man and his environment. This too, is a consequence of technological progress – new medical techniques removing pestilence and improving sanitation, producing a fall in the death rate at birth and an increase in the length of life. In 1870 the average length of life in developed countries was 43 years, today it is 68 years. At present, the world's population stands at 3 500 million, and is increasing by 63 million per year. It took 50 000 years for mankind to reach this total. It will take only another 33 years to double it. The rate of increase in the last few centuries has been phenomenal. One authority estimates that of the 77 billion births since the stone age, 30 per cent have been in the last three centuries and that of the total number of people ever born 4 per cent are now living.[9] In 1850, the world's population stood at 1 billion, 75 years later (1925) it was 2 billion, and 37 years after that (1962) 3 billion. By 1977 (15 years later) it will be 4 billion, and ten years after that 5 billion. If the population of India continues to grow at its present rate then in 100 years it will equal the present population of the world. Whatever is done now to stabilize the population by stamping out ignorance, removing religious taboos, and changing national policies, in regard to birth control techniques, the fact must be faced that by the end of this century there will 7 billion people on the earth, and, barring an apocalyptic catastrophe, 20 billion in a hundred years time. This much seems certain; beyond is uncertain, but if the population continues to grow at its present rate – 2 per cent per year – then there will be 50 billion within 140 years. This, be it noted, is the highest estimate of the earth's capacity – with highly advanced technology – made by any responsible scholar.[10] Whatever the final figure of people reached, all will have their rising expectations, and all will put increasing pressure on land and other resources – many of which are non-renewable. Malthus' forebodings have so far proved unfounded because he underestimated the rate of tech-

nological progress and its impact on geography – expanding
our resource-base and permitting the earth to sustain an ever
growing population with higher standards of living. Technology has so far kept abreast of this exponential growth in
population but the Food and Agricultural Organization has
warned that food production is beginning to fall behind population increase, and that large-scale famines must be expected
before 1980 unless something drastic is done. Half the world's
citizens are already undernourished. Yet there is little doubt
that with the full exploitation of existing technology the world
could accommodate a very sizeable population. Indeed, for the
first time in history we either have, or are in the process of acquiring, the knowledge to eliminate all the old biblical maledic-
tions and to allow the human race to live, materially,
comfortably ever after. Or, as Julian Huxley once expressed
it, 'to move from the struggle for survival, to the struggle for
fulfilment.' But whether in fact we shall be able to take advantage of the new mastery over our conditions will depend
on whether we can organize ourselves in a way and on a scale
which will allow us to exploit the tools we now possess, use
them to correct the imbalances we have caused, and plan and
manage the developing world on a global basis. To take one
example of the problems we face from the increasing pressure
on resources. It is estimated that the world has fossil fuel reserves of up to 500 million million tons, but because of the
poisonous effects of combustion products we can, at the
moment, only afford to burn about 13 million million tons.[11]

Several visionary schemes have been put forward to enhance
the world's resource base. Russian engineers have a plan to
block the Bering Straits between Siberia and Alaska. This dam
would be equipped with batteries of giant pumps which would
draw vast quantities of cold water from the Arctic Ocean into
the Pacific. This would cause the Gulf Stream in the Atlantic
to carry its warm water around the north of Canada, melting
the polar sea-ice and opening up the vast mineral wealth of these
regions to exploitation. The precise effect of this plan on the
climate of countries on and around the Arctic Circle is not

known. But Britain and North-Western Europe depend upon the Gulf Stream for their temperate weather. Without it, Britain's climate would be very similar to Labrador's.

Another ambitious scheme involving the Mediterranean has been put forward by a German engineer. This too, would have profound economic and political repercussions. The Mediterranean Sea loses millions of cubic feet of water each year through evaporation. Most of the loss is replenished from the Atlantic. By damming the Straits of Gibraltar and sealing off the Black Sea at the Dardanelles, the level of water in the Mediterranean would fall at the rate of 3 ft a year or 330 ft in one hundred years. Countries bordering the inland sea would acquire huge areas of new land (about 220 000 sq. miles in all) for cultivation and industrial development, and dams built across the mouths of rivers flowing into the sea would provide a source of cheap hydro-electric power on a gigantic scale. Another proposal of the same German engineer is to dam the Congo river near its mouth, converting the Congo basin and Lake Chad into a vast inland sea, watering the Sahara, and connected to the Mediterranean by a river.

Man-made alterations to the geography of a region on this scale would have cumulative effects encroaching on other regions. Yet although for the present these ideas remain visionary, there is no doubt that eventually these schemes, or other technological operations of comparable magnitude, will be needed.

According to Soviet scientists there is another problem facing us, arising from energy use. 'The problem we shall have to solve in the future will not be so much the shortage of power as excess of it. If man continues to acquire new power supplies at the same rate as hitherto, according to some calculations, within a few decades the amount of man-made heat resulting from the production process will reach a considerable figure and ultimately be comparable with that received by the earth from the sun. When that time comes, the heat balance of the earth will have to be changed, and we shall have to learn how to evacuate a substantial quantity of energy into space if we are going to prevent the earth's surface from being gravely overheated. . . .'[12]

Man's intervention in the course of natural processes is becoming more and more considerable. It is already substantial in relation to the fluctuations that occur in natural processes, and the time is not so far away when it will be comparable to and then will surpass natural changes. In his address to the delegates of the UN Conference on Science and Technology for Development, the Soviet scientist, Academician E. K. Federov, summed up the whole position: 'There is no danger of a scantiness of natural resources, but there does exist another danger – that is their spontaneous, unorganized utilization.

'It is high time for all of us to pass from the primitive "hunting" economy to a regulated cultivation of natural resources on the earth as a whole. Should we fail to do this in the circumstances of the growing influence upon nature we run the risk of wasting thriftlessly the earth's resources; we risk taking the whole complex of natural processes out of that state of mobile equilibrium in which it exists now, and to transform it into some other state that may be undesirable for us all.

'The human society has become such a mighty force in the life of our planet, that already it cannot permit unorganized actions anywhere on the earth or outside of it.'[13]

*

It is easy to dismiss all this as 'alarmist', 'far-out', and 'futuristic' – quite unworthy of serious commentary. But is this really so? Some of these problems are already upon us, and are others really so very much more fantastic than, say, a 'man on the moon' would have seemed ten or twenty years ago? Are we to persist in underestimating, as we have in the past, the speed of technological progress? Can we afford to ignore the advise of some of our most eminent scientists? – all perfectly sane, and essentially practical men. And even if the optimistic view is taken and these problems are relegated to a hundred or a hundred and fifty years hence, when measuring the pace of political change against the accelerating speed of technological progress, it is possible to grasp the critical position we are in. Can we produce the required adjustment with the necessary speed.

And what has all this got to do with the movement to unite Europe? Just this. If we are to create a stable relationship between man and his environment, the world will have to put an end to the present anarchy, develop suitable new political forms and procedures transcending the national framework, and learn to organize itself on a scale consonant with the dimensions of modern technology in a shrinking world. In considering European unity in a technological perspective it is proper to examine whether a regional movement of this kind is likely to advance or impede progress towards wider international solidarity. If, in building a United Europe, we are simply building regional groupings which are going to end up by dividing the world into a few large blocks with a strong streak of continental nationalism, perhaps with racialist undertones such as we see in Africa and the Middle East, then it might be better to abandon the project and revert to the universalist approach, unsatisfactory and exasperating as progress at that level has so far proved to be.

It is undeniable that Europe has strong 'third force', autarkic characteristics. By a sense of exclusion rather than comprehension, it gains cohesion and impetus. Indeed, in so far as the movement is an attempt to escape from a position of dependence it is a vote in favour of independence. But a measure of independence does not exclude a policy of interdependence. On the contrary, successful partnership requires a degree of equality. It is also true that the Community has begun to acquire a built-in autonomy. As the process of economic integration gains momentum the accession of new members becomes more difficult to realize both from the point of view of existing members and from the point of view of those countries wishing to join. Members acquire a vested interest in the policies accepted and there is the danger of encumbering the Community and hindering its progress by watering down its character and personality, curbing and even eliminating its dynamism. At the same time it is difficult for prospective members to accept the rules and agreements which they have had no hand in implementing and in the formulation of which their interests have not been taken into account. There also appears to be a certain 'optimum size' for such a Community beyond which the administrative machinery becomes too cumbersome to reconcile conflicting interests and preserve a balance. General de Gaulle emphasized these problems in his latest press conference: 'For our part, there is no question of a veto... It is simply a question of finding out whether this conclusion is possible within the framework of the Common Market without bringing about destructive upheavals: or in what other situation and in what other conditions this conclusion could be possible. . . . I have spoken of destructive upheavals in the Common Market. We all know that it has taken ten years to construct it and also an untiring effort of cooperation on the part of the Six. . . . In short, the Common Market is a sort of miracle. At this point to introduce new massive elements among those which have so painfully been agreed upon, would clearly mean putting into question the whole structure and its components and raising the problem of a completely different undertaking.'[14]

But against all this must be set the aims and ideals of the founders of modern Europe. For them it was not just a question of creating a new great power but of pioneering a new method of international order in Europe and beyond. President Kennedy certainly saw a United Europe as a means towards solving some of the larger problems of the world. 'We believe that a United Europe will be capable of playing a greater role in the common defence, of responding more generously to the needs of poorer nations. . . . We see such a Europe as a partner with whom the United States could deal on a basis of full equality in all the great and burdensome tasks of building and defending a community of free nations.'[15] But it is Jean Monnet himself who has expressed most clearly what he was seeking to achieve in building a United States of Europe: '. . . unity in Europe does not create a new kind of great power; it is a method of introducing change in Europe and consequently in the world. People... are tempted to see the European Community as a potential 19th century state with all the overtones of power this implies. But we are not in the 19th century, and the Europeans have built up the European Community precisely in order to find a way out of the conflicts to which the 19th century power philosophy gave rise. The natural attitude of a European Community based on the exercise by nations of common responsibilities will be to make these nations also aware of their responsibilities, as a Community, to the world. ... European unity is not a blueprint, it is not a theory, it is a process that has already begun, of bringing peoples and nations together to adapt themselves jointly to changing circumstances.

'European unity is the most important event in the West since the war, not because it is a new great power, but because the new institutional method it introduces is permanently modifying relations between nations and men. Human nature does not change, but when nations and men accept the same rules and the same institutions to make sure that they are applied, their behaviour towards each other changes. This is the process of civilization itself.'[16]

Whether or not Monnet's faith and vision will be fulfilled has yet to be determined. Ultimately, it must depend on the courage, patience, flexibility, and wisdom of our political leaders. Such as they are it is not always possible to be optimistic. And the lead time for survival is not so very long.

NOTES

One

[1] HORNELL HART, 'Technology and the Growth of Political Areas' in *Technology and International Relations*. Edited by William Ogburn. (Chicago University Press, 1949).

[2] Source: *United Nations Statistical Yearbook*. 1966.

[3] 'Why not "pipe" people?', *New Scientist*. October 7th 1965.

[4] 'Pegasus Rocket Transport', *Spaceflight*. No. 2, March 1965.

[5] 'Conversations Encoded', *New Scientist*. July 28th 1966.

[6] 'Work of the Plan Committee in the Intercontinental Sphere', *Telecommunications Journal*. Vol. 31, April 1964.

[7] Source: *World Communications*. UNESCO. 1964. extrapolated.

[8] Ibid.

[9] 'Extra Terrestial Relays', *Wireless World*. October 1945.

[10] Source: *The World's Telephones*, 1966. American Telephone & Telegraph Co.

[11] 'New Techniques of Communication', *Discovery*. Vol. 25, October 1964.

[12] 'Computing power for everyman', *New Scientist*. September 29th 1966.

[13] 'Applications of Lasers to Telecommunications' *Telecommunications Journal*. Vol. 32. October 1965.

[14] 'World Communication', *Journal of the Royal Society of Arts*. February 1966.

[15] 'The Age of Automation', Reith Lectures. *Listener*. November 19th 1964.

Two

[1] Cf. 'Power without wires,' *Electronics Weekly*. December 1964 and 'Power by Radio', *New Scientist*. June 10th 1965.

[2] Cf. *CERN Courier*. No. 6, Vol. 6, June, 1966.

[3] 'Translating and transcoding between colour-TV systems with common scanning standards', *Proceedings of the Institution of Electrical Engineers*. Vol. 114, January 1967.

[4] GUNNAR MYRDAL, *An International Economy*. (Routledge & Kegan Paul, 1956) & *Beyond the Welfare State*. (Duckworth, 1960).

Three

[1] in RICHARD MAYNE, *The Community of Europe*. (Gollancz, 1963). which is also a useful introduction to the Community.

[2] GEOFFREY BARRACLOUGH, *European Unity in Thought and Action*. (Blackwell, 1963).

[3] J. R. SEELEY, *The Expansion of England*. (Macmillan & Co. 1885).

[4] A. MAHAN, *The Influence of Sea Power Upon History*. (Boston, 1890).

[5]   SIR H. MACKINDER, 'The Geographical Pivot of History', *Geographical Journal*. No. 23, April 1904.

[6]   SIR H. MACKINDER, 'The Round World and Winning of Peace', *Foreign Affairs*. July 1943.

[7]   Cf. *Geographical Journal*. No. 23, April 1904. p. 441. The italics are the author's. An interesting review of geopolitics and technological progress is H. SPROUT. 'Geopolitical Hypotheses in Technological Perspective', *World Politics*. January 1963.

[8]   ALEXIS DE TOCQUEVILLE, *Democracy in America*. translated by Henry Reeve, Vol. 2 (Saunders & Otley, 1835), p. 455–457.

[9]   R.N. COUDENHOVE-KALERGI, *Pan Europe*. (New York, 1926).

[10]   E. HERRIOT, *A United States of Europe*. (Harrap, 1930).

[11]   Cf. SIR O. MOSLEY, *Europe: Faith and Plan*. (Euphorion Books, 1958).

[12]   *Customs Unions:* A League of Nations Contribution to the Study of Customs Union Problems. (UNO, New York, 1947) p. 47.

[13]   RICHARD MAYNE, 'Economic Integration in the New Europe', *Daedalus* Vol. 93, Winter 1964.

Four

[1]   B. LIDDELL HART, 'The Ratio of Forces to Space' in *Deterrent or Defence*. (Stevens & Sons, 1960).

[2]   A. BUCHAN & P. WINDSOR, *Arms and Stability in Europe*. (Institute of Strategic Studies. 1963). p. 223.

[3]   Cf. R. STRAUSZ-HUPÉ, *The Balance of Tomorrow*. (Putnam's Sons, New York 1945).

[4]   The most complete analysis of size and economic performance is, *Economic Consequences of the Size of Nations*. Edited by E. A. G. Robinson. (Macmillan & Co. 1960). An important study on the issue in relation to international integration is, BELA BALASSA, *The Theory of Economic Integration*. (Allen & Unwin Ltd, 1961).

[5]   Cf. T. SCITOVSKY, *Economic Theory and Western European Integration*. (Stanford University Press, 1958).

[6]   *Comité intergouvernemental créé par la Conférence de Messine*. (Brussels, 1956) pp. 13-14. (Translation, R. Mayne. *Daedalus* Vol. 93, Winter 1964).

[7]   *Science, Economic Growth and Government Policy*. (OECD, Paris 1963).

[8]   B. F. MASSELL, 'Capital Formation and Technological Change in U.S. Manufacturing', *Review of Economics and Statistics*. May 1960.

[9]   C. FREEMAN et al., *The Research and Development Effort in Western Europe, N. America and the Soviet Union*. (OECD, Paris 1965).

[10]   Source: 'Overseas Royalty Transactions in 1964', *Board of Trade Journal*. July 29th 1966.

[11]   A valuable contribution to the brain-drain phenomenon is S. DEDIJER, 'Why did Daedalus Leave?'. *Science*. Vol. 137, June 30th 1961.

[12]   *Research and Development Effort*. (OECD, Paris 1965). p. 51.

[13]   C. D. EDWARDS, 'Size and Competition' in *Economic Consequences of the Size of Nations*. (Macmillan & Co, 1963). p. 129.

[14] Cf. B. R. WILLIAMS, 'Investment and Technology in Growth', *Manchester School of Economic and Social Studies*. March 1964.

[15] A. SHONFIELD, 'A Deadlock on the Left', *Encounter*. September 1959.

[16] B. K. BLOUNT, 'Science will change the Balance of Power', *New Scientist*. June 28th 1957.

[17] For a more moderate view of input-output cf. J. JEWKES, 'How Much Science?' *Economic Journal*. March 1960.

[18] B. R. WILLIAMS, *Industrial Research and Economic Growth in Australia*. (Adelaide, 1962).

[19] Euratom, *Seventh General Report*. March 1964. p. 27.

[20] J. H. DUNNING, *American Investment in British Manufacturing Industry*. (London, 1958).

[21] 'Overseas Royalty Transactions in 1964', *Board of Trade Journal*, July 1966.

[22] Stanford Research Institute. *R & D in Europe*. Long range planning report. No. 198.

[23] This view is also supported by C. FREEMAN, 'Research and Development in Electronic Capital Goods', NIESR *Economic Review*. November 1965.

[24] Cf. R. SOLO, 'Gearing Military R & D to Economic Growth', *Harvard Business Review*. December 1962.

[25] D. FISHLOCK, 'The 'fall-out' from the Space Race', *New Scientist*. May 30th. 1963.

[26] For an account of the spin-off argument as a justification of the U.S. space programme Cf. VERNON VAN DYKE, *Pride and Power*. (University of Illinois 1964).

[27] J. WELLES et al, *The Commercial Application of Missle/Space Technology*. (University of Denver 1963).

[28] 'Fall-out: Fact or Fantasy?', *Engineering*. July 23rd 1965.

[29] Euratom. *Seventh General Report*. March 1964. Cf. also, D. FISHLOCK, 'Fall-out from Nuclear Research', *New Scientist*. November 18th 1965.

[30] *Report of the Committee of Inquiry into the Aircraft Industry*. HMSO. 1965, Cmnd. 2853. Ch. 14.

[31] UNICE. *Certains Aspects des Disparités dans les Dimensions des plus Grandes Enterprises de la CEE, Comparées avec leurs Principaux Concurrents des Pays Tiers*. (Brussels 1965).

[32] Cf. 'Research and Development: a comparison between British and American Industry', NIESR *Economic Review*. May 1962.

[33] *Industrial Concentration and Product Diversification*. Federal Trade Commission, 1957.

[34] J. SCHUMPETER, *Capitalism, Socialism and Democracy*. (New York, 1943). and J. GALBRAITH. *American Capitalism*. (Hamish Hamilton, 1957).

[35] E. MANSFIELD, 'Industrial Research and Development Expenditures', *Journal of Political Economy*. August 1964.

[36] F. SCHERER, 'Firm size and the output of patented inventions', *American Economic Review*. December 1965.

[37] Cf. J. JEWKES et al, *The Sources of Invention*. (Macmillan & Co, 1961).

[38] C. FREEMAN, 'The Plastics Industry', NIESR *Economic Review*. November 1963.

[39] Source: C. FREEMAN, 'Research and Development in Electronic

Capital Goods, NIESR *Economic Review*. November 1965. which contains an excellent account of the lead time problem.

[40]   Cf. R. NELSON, 'Economics of Parallel R & D Efforts', *Review of Economics and Statistics*. November 1961. see also, *The Rate and Direction of Inventive Activity*. Part V. (Princeton, 1960).

[41]   Cf. G. W. NUTTER, 'Monopoly, Bigness and Progress', *Journal of Political Economy*. December 1956. H. VILLARD, 'Competition, Bigness and Research', *Journal of Political Economy*. December 1958. J. SCHMOOKLER, 'Bigness, Fewness and Research', *Journal of Political Economy*. December 1959, and VILLARD's reply.

[42]   F. WOODWARD, *Structure of Industrial Research Associations*. OECD. Paris 1965.

[43]   C. FREEMAN, 'Research and Development in Electronic Capital Goods', NIESR *Economic Review*. November 1965. see also, P. M. S. BLACKETT, *Technology, Industry and Economic Growth*. (University of Southampton, 1966).

[44]   *Government Purchasing*. OECD, Paris 1966.

[45]   *The Report of the Committee of Inquiry into the Aircraft Industry*. HMSO 1965. Cmnd. 2853. Ch. 4.

Five

[1]   G. PALEWSKI, 'La Politique de recherche scientifique de la France', *Le Progrès Scientifique*. No. 63. DGRST, Paris, December 1963.

[2]   G. PALEWSKI, 'Politique de la Science', *Nouvelle Frontière*. No. 8, October 1964.

[3]   'Recherche Scientifique et Indépendance', *Le Progrès Scientifique*. No. 76, DGRST, Paris, September 1964.

[4]   For details on the organization and policy of science in individual countries cf. *Country Reports* and *Reviews of National Science Policy*. OECD. Paris.

[5]   'De-Gaulle's Techno-Diplomacy', *New Scientist*. July 7th 1966.

[6]   A useful guide to the major science organizations is, *International Scientific Organizations*. OECD, Paris, 1965. see especially the Introduction.

[7]   *Report on Increasing the Effectiveness of Western Science*. (Fondation Universitaire, Brussels 1960). *Proposal for the Establishment of an International Institute of Science and Technology*. Paris, November 1962.

[8]   Cf. the Annual Reports of EURATOM. and J. G. POLACH, *Euratom*. (Oceana Publications, New York 1964.) For details on the organization of nuclear energy and progress in its development cf. *Atomic Handbook: Europe*. (Morgan Brothers, London 1965).

[9]   Cf. *The Fifteenth General Report of ECSC*. 1966—67.

[10]   The *Second Report from the Estimates Committee on ELDO* 1966–67. August 1966 HMSO. L. SHEPHERD & A. V. CLEAVER 'A Future for ELDO', *New Scientist*. February 24th 1966. A useful round-up of Europe's current space activities is, K. W. GATLAND, 'Europe in Space', *Spaceflight*. May 1966.

[11]   A. KING, 'Science and Technology in the New Europe', *Daedalus* Vol. 93. Winter 1964. cf. also S. WILLIAMS, 'European Unity and Technological Cooperation', *European Community*. March 1966. J-J. SALOMON, 'International Science Policy', *Minerva*. Summer 1964.

J-J. SALOMON, 'Problems of International Cooperation in Scientific and Technical Research', *OECD Observer*. February 1966.

[12]   J. A. ROBBINS, 'Is Standardization a Common Market Trade Barrier?' *Electrical Times*. March 31st 1966. 'Traps for the Europe-Wise Engineer', *Engineering*, October 29th, 1965.

[13]   *Translation of a Draft Convention relating to a European Patent Law*. HMSO. 1962.

[14]   *Public Purchasing and Industrial Efficiency*. HMSO. May 1967. Cmnd. 3291.

[15]   J. CALMANN, *European Integration in Defence Technology*. (Institute of Strategic Studies. March 1967).

[16]   The *Report of the Netherlands State-Secretary for Economic Affairs to the Second Chamber of the States-General*. June 7th 1966.

[17]   P. VERLOREN VAN THEMAAT, 'Problems of Scale and Mergers in the Common Market' in *Problems of Scale in Europe*. (Federal Trust, 1966).

[18]   Cf, *ECC Commission Memorandum on the Creation of a European Company*. Brussels, April 1966. SEC(66)1250.

[19]   Cf. The speech of H. VAN DER GROEBEN to the European Parliament. June 16th 1965.

[20]   D. SWANN & D. L. MCLACHLAN, *Concentration or Competition: A European Dilemma?* PEP/Chatham House. January 1967.

[21]   *Preliminary Draft of the First Medium-Term Economic Policy Programme*. 1966–1970. Brussels., March 1966. 787/11/1966–E.

[22]   Cf. *Report on the proposal of the resolution relating to a European Common Scientific Policy*. Rapporteur: M. SCHUIJT. European Parliament, Document 107. October 12th 1966.

[23]   *Memorandum of the French Government on Scientific and Technical Research*. Agence Europe. No. 309. March 16th 1965.

[24]   *Report on technological progress and scientific research in the European Community*. Rapporteur: M. OELE. European Parliament. Document 97. September 23rd 1966.

[25]   The debate on a common science policy European Parliament. October 18th 1966.

[26]   *Memorandum on the problems posed by scientific and technological progress in the European Community*. Brussels, March 20th 1967. EUR/C/1711/2/67–F.

[27]   For the American point of view cf. DR A. T. KNOPPERS, '*The Role of Science and Technology in Atlantic Economic Relationships*'. Atlantic Institute. May 1966. and R. MCNAMARA, 'A Technology Gap or a Management Gap?' *NATO Newsletter*. April 1967.

[28]   *Fundamental Research and the Policies of Governments*. OECD, Paris 1966. Ch. 9. Special Proposals.

[29]   Presidential Address to the Royal Society. November 1965.

[30]   Cf. for example, C. LAYTON, *Trans-Atlantic Investments*. Atlantic Institute. 1966. p. 101 and C. LAYTON, *A Common Policy for Europe in Science and Technology*. PEP paper. 1967.

[31]   *A Smaller Stage*. (Bow Publications, 1965).

[32]   SIR ANTHONY MEYER, *A European Technological Community*. CPC. December 1966.

[33]   *The Resolution relative to a European Common Scientific Policy*. European Parliament. Document 63. May 1966.

[34]   *Hansard*. November 17th 1966.

[35]   'Federalism *à la carte*', *European Community*. March 1966.

[36]   *Science and the Policies of Governments*, OECD. September 1963. p. 47.

[37]   GUNNAR MYRDAL, *Realities and Illusions in Regard to Inter-Governmental Organizations.* Hobhouse Memorial Lecture. (O.U.P., 1955). © London School of Economics.

[38]   G. PALEWSKI, 'A Scientific Research Policy in the World of Today', *Science and Parliament.* OECD/Council of Europe. May 1965.

Six

[1]   DR JOHN VON NEUMANN, 'Can we survive technology?' *Fortune LI.* June 1955. p. 106.

[2]   SIR BERNARD LOVELL. *Sunday Times.* Weekly Review. March 16th 1964.

[3]   *Weather and Climate Modification: problems and prospects.* National Research Council. Washington, 1966.

[4]   Cf. *Science.* Vol. 154, p. 1555.

[5]   *Restoring the Quality of Our Environment.* President's Science Advisory Committee. Washington, November 1965. This report is an excellent source of information on environmental contamination

[6]   DR J. M. STAGG, 'Atmospheric Contamination and Climatic Stability', *New Scientist.* September 10th 1964.

[7]   *Ecology and the Industrial Society.* Edited by G. T. Goodman et al, (Blackwell, 1966).

[8]   B. COMMONER, *Science and Survival.* (Gollancz, 1966) p. 110.

[9]   P. HAUSER, 'Man and more men: population prospects', *Bulletin of Atomic Scientists.* June 1964.

[10]   H. BROWN, *The Challenge of Man's Future.* (Secker & Warburg, 1954).

[11]   See the letter from HARALD KLEPP, 'How much can we burn?' in *New Scientist.* October 7th 1965.

[12]   E. K. FEDEROV, 'Some problems relating to developing countries', *Impact.* Vol. 13, No. 4, UNESCO 1963.

[13]   E. K. FEDEROV, Address to the plenary session. *UN Conference on Science and Technology for Development.* Vol. 8, Plenary Proceedings. (UNO, New York, February 1963).

[14]   DE-GAULLE's Press Conference. May 16th 1967. *The Times.* May 17th 1967.

[15]   J. F. KENNEDY, *Declaration of Interdependence.* Philadelphia. USA. July 4th 1962.

[16]   J. MONNET, 'A Ferment of Change', *Journal of Common Market Studies.* Vol. 1, No. 3, p. 211.

Index

206